OFFICIAL SQA PAST PAPERS

WITH ANSWERS

STANDARD GRADE | CREDIT

PHYSICS
2007-2011

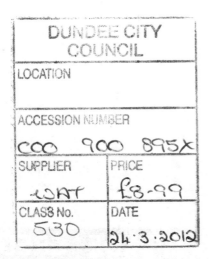
Publisher's Note

We are delighted to bring you the 2011 Past Papers and you will see that we have changed the format from previous editions. As part of our environmental awareness strategy, we have attempted to make these new editions as sustainable as possible.

To do this, we have printed on white paper and bound the answer sections into the book. This not only allows us to use significantly less paper but we are also, for the first time, able to source all the materials from sustainable sources.

We hope you like the new editions and by purchasing this product, you are not only supporting an independent Scottish publishing company but you are also, in the International Year of Forests, not contributing to the destruction of the world's forests.

Thank you for your support and please see the following websites for more information to support the above statement –

www.fsc-uk.org

www.loveforests.com

© Scottish Qualifications Authority
All rights reserved. Copying prohibited. No part of this publication may be reproduced, stored in a retrieval system, or transmitted in any form or by any means, electronic, mechanical, photocopying, recording or otherwise.

First exam published in 2007.
Published by Bright Red Publishing Ltd, 6 Stafford Street, Edinburgh EH3 7AU
tel: 0131 220 5804 fax: 0131 220 6710 info@brightredpublishing.co.uk www.brightredpublishing.co.uk

ISBN 978-1-84948-180-9

A CIP Catalogue record for this book is available from the British Library.

Bright Red Publishing is grateful to the copyright holders, as credited on the final page of the Question Section, for permission to use their material. Every effort has been made to trace the copyright holders and to obtain their permission for the use of copyright material.
Bright Red Publishing will be happy to receive information allowing us to rectify any error or omission in future editions.

STANDARD GRADE | CREDIT
2007

[BLANK PAGE]

C

FOR OFFICIAL USE

K & U	PS

Total Marks

3220/402

NATIONAL
QUALIFICATIONS
2007

WEDNESDAY, 16 MAY
10.50 AM – 12.35 PM

PHYSICS
STANDARD GRADE
Credit Level

Fill in these boxes and read what is printed below.

Full name of centre

Town

Forename(s)

Surname

Date of birth

Day   Month   Year   Scottish candidate number   Number of seat

Reference may be made to the Physics Data Booklet.

1 All questions should be answered.

2 The questions may be answered in any order but all answers must be written clearly and legibly in this book.

3 Write your answer where indicated by the question or in the space provided after the question.

4 If you change your mind about your answer you may score it out and rewrite it in the space provided at the end of the answer book.

5 Before leaving the examination room you must give this book to the invigilator. If you do not, you may lose all the marks for this paper.

6 Any necessary data will be found in the **data sheet** on page two.

7 Care should be taken to give an appropriate number of significant figures in the final answers to questions.

SCOTTISH
QUALIFICATIONS
AUTHORITY

©

DATA SHEET

Speed of light in materials

Material	Speed in m/s
Air	$3 \cdot 0 \times 10^8$
Carbon dioxide	$3 \cdot 0 \times 10^8$
Diamond	$1 \cdot 2 \times 10^8$
Glass	$2 \cdot 0 \times 10^8$
Glycerol	$2 \cdot 1 \times 10^8$
Water	$2 \cdot 3 \times 10^8$

Speed of sound in materials

Material	Speed in m/s
Aluminium	5200
Air	340
Bone	4100
Carbon dioxide	270
Glycerol	1900
Muscle	1600
Steel	5200
Tissue	1500
Water	1500

Gravitational field strengths

	Gravitational field strength on the surface in N/kg
Earth	10
Jupiter	26
Mars	4
Mercury	4
Moon	1·6
Neptune	12
Saturn	11
Sun	270
Venus	9

Specific heat capacity of materials

Material	Specific heat capacity in J/kg °C
Alcohol	2350
Aluminium	902
Copper	386
Diamond	530
Glass	500
Glycerol	2400
Ice	2100
Lead	128
Water	4180

Specific latent heat of fusion of materials

Material	Specific latent heat of fusion in J/kg
Alcohol	$0 \cdot 99 \times 10^5$
Aluminium	$3 \cdot 95 \times 10^5$
Carbon dioxide	$1 \cdot 80 \times 10^5$
Copper	$2 \cdot 05 \times 10^5$
Glycerol	$1 \cdot 81 \times 10^5$
Lead	$0 \cdot 25 \times 10^5$
Water	$3 \cdot 34 \times 10^5$

Melting and boiling points of materials

Material	Melting point in °C	Boiling point in °C
Alcohol	−98	65
Aluminium	660	2470
Copper	1077	2567
Glycerol	18	290
Lead	328	1737
Turpentine	−10	156

Specific latent heat of vaporisation of materials

Material	Specific latent heat of vaporisation in J/kg
Alcohol	$11 \cdot 2 \times 10^5$
Carbon dioxide	$3 \cdot 77 \times 10^5$
Glycerol	$8 \cdot 30 \times 10^5$
Turpentine	$2 \cdot 90 \times 10^5$
Water	$22 \cdot 6 \times 10^5$

SI Prefixes and Multiplication Factors

Prefix	Symbol	Factor	
giga	G	1 000 000 000	$= 10^9$
mega	M	1 000 000	$= 10^6$
kilo	k	1000	$= 10^3$
milli	m	0·001	$= 10^{-3}$
micro	μ	0·000 001	$= 10^{-6}$
nano	n	0·000 000 001	$= 10^{-9}$

DO NOT
WRITE IN
THIS
MARGIN

Marks	K&U	PS

1. A pupil is sent exam results by a text message on a mobile phone. The frequency of the signal received by the phone is 1900 MHz.

The mobile phone receives radio waves (signals).

(a) What is the speed of radio waves?

3×10^8 m/s

1

(b) Calculate the wavelength of the signal.

Space for working and answer

$\lambda = v/f$

$\lambda = 3 \times 10^8 / 1900$

$\lambda = 0.16$ m

2

(c) The pupil sends a video message from the mobile phone. The message is transmitted by microwaves. The message travels a total distance of 72 000 km.

Calculate the time between the message being transmitted and received.

Space for working and answer

$t = D/v$

$t = 72000'/3 \times 10^8$

$t = 0.24$ s

2

Marks | K&U | PS

2. Radio waves have a wide range of frequencies.

The table gives information about different wavebands.

Waveband	Frequency Range	Example
Low frequency (LF)	30 kHz – 300 kHz	Radio 4
Medium frequency (MF)	300 kHz – 3 MHz	Radio Scotland
High frequency (HF)	3 MHz – 30 MHz	Amateur radio
Very high frequency (VHF)	30 MHz – 300 MHz	Radio 1 FM
Ultra high frequency (UHF)	300 MHz – 3 GHz	BBC 1 and ITV
Super high frequency (SHF)	3 GHz – 30 GHz	Satellite TV

(a) Coastguards use signals of frequency 500 kHz.

What waveband do these signals belong to?

_____ Radio Scotland, medium _____

1

2. (continued)

(b) The diagram shows how radio signals of different wavelengths are sent between a transmitter and a receiver.

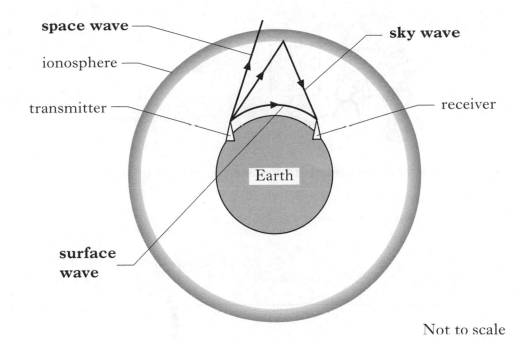

Not to scale

(i) Which of the waves in the diagram shows diffraction?

Surface wave

1

(ii) What does this indicate about the wavelength of the diffracted wave compared to the other two waves?

it is the same size

1

(iii) The Earth's ionosphere is shown on the diagram. The ionosphere is a layer of charged particles in the upper atmosphere. High frequency waves are transmitted as sky waves.

Explain how the transmitted waves reach the receiver.

The transmitted wave bounce off the ionosphere

1

(iv) Super high frequency (SHF) signals are shown as space waves on the diagram. Although they can only travel in straight lines, they can be used for communications on Earth between a transmitter and receiver.

Describe how the SHF signals get to the receiver.

They are Bounced off of a Satellite and are sent back to the receiver

2

Marks K&U PS

Marks | K&U | PS

3. A door entry system in an office block allows video and audio information to be sent between two people.

(a) A camera at the entrance uses a lens to focus parallel rays of light onto a detector.

Part of the camera is shown in the diagram below.

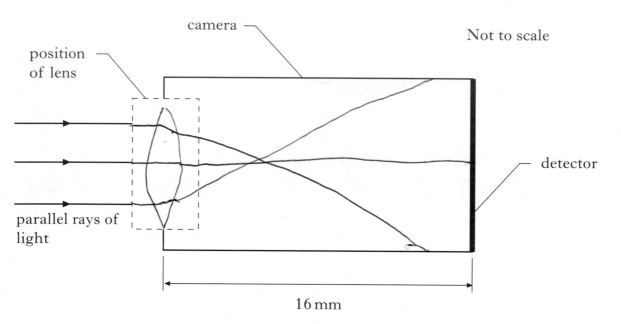

16 mm

(i) Complete the diagram above by:

(A)   drawing the lens used;

(B)   completing the path of the light rays.

2

(ii) Using information from the diagram, calculate the power of the lens used in the camera.

Space for working and answer

2

Marks | K&U | PS

3. **(continued)**

(b) The door entry system uses a black and white television screen.

Describe how a moving picture is seen on the television screen.

Your description must include the terms:

line build up   **image retention**   **brightness variation**.

....

....

....

....

....

.... 3

[Turn over

Marks | K&U | PS

4. The consumer unit in a house contains a mains switch and circuit breakers for different circuits.

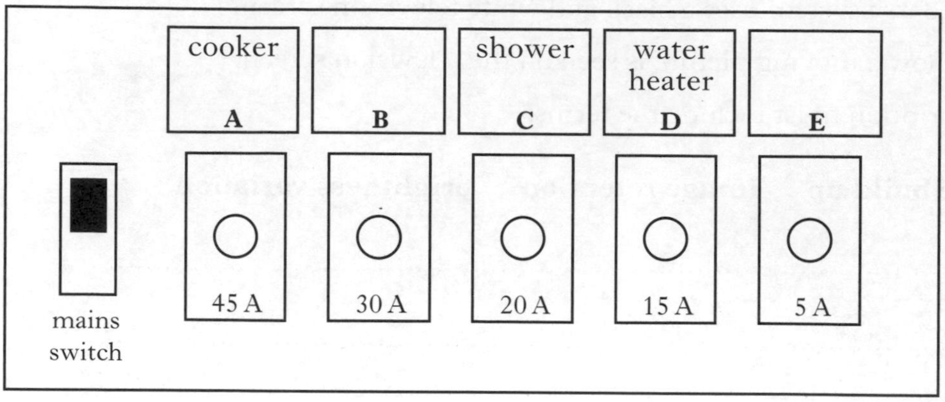

	cooker			shower	water heater	
mains switch	A	B	C	D	E
	45 A	30 A	20 A	15 A	5 A

(a) (i) What is the purpose of the mains switch?

to switch off every circuit

1

(ii) Two of the circuits have not been labelled.

Which circuit is: the ring circuit?   B

the lighting circuit?   E

1

(iii) The current ratings for the ring circuit and the lighting circuit are different.

State another difference between the ring circuit and the lighting circuit.

the wire is bigger in a
Ring circuit

1

DO NOT WRITE IN THIS MARGIN

Marks	K&U	PS

4. (continued)

(*b*) (i) A 25 W lamp is designed to be used with mains voltage.

Calculate the resistance of the lamp.

Space for working and answer

R =

R = V/.

R =

R =

3

(ii) Four of these lamps are connected in parallel.

Calculate the **total** resistance of the lamps.

Space for working and answer

2

[Turn over

Marks | K&U | PS

5. Two groups of pupils are investigating the electrical properties of a lamp.

(a) Group 1 is given the following equipment:

ammeter; voltmeter; 12 V d.c. supply; lamp; connecting leads.

Complete the circuit diagram to show how this equipment is used to measure the current through, and the voltage across, the lamp.

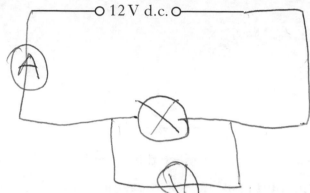

○ 12 V d.c. ○

3

(b) Group 2 uses the same lamp and is only given the following equipment:

lamp; ohmmeter; connecting leads.

What property of the lamp is measured by the ohmmeter?

...........Resistance...........

1

(c) The results of both groups are combined and recorded in the table below.

I(A)	V(V)	R(Ω)	IV	I^2R
2	12	6		

(i) Use these results to complete the last two columns of the table.

Space for working $IV = 24$ $I^2R = 24$

2

(ii) What quantity is represented by the last two columns of the table?

Power

....

1

(iii) What is the unit for this quantity?

watts

....

1

Marks | K&U | PS

6. The thyroid gland, located in the neck, is essential for maintaining good health.

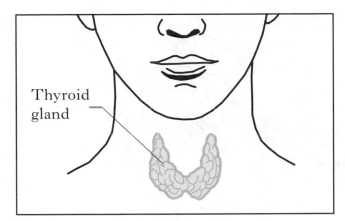

Thyroid gland

(*a*) (i) A radioactive source, which is a gamma radiation emitter, is used as a radioactive tracer for the diagnosis of thyroid gland disorders.

A small quantity of this tracer, with an activity of 20 MBq, is injected into a patient's body. After 52 hours, the activity of the tracer is measured at 1·25 MBq.

Calculate the half life of the tracer.

> *Space for working and answer*   13 hours
>
> working

2

(ii) Another radioactive source is used to **treat** cancer of the thyroid gland. This source emits only beta radiation.

Why is this source unsuitable as a **tracer**?

....

.... 1

(iii) The equivalent dose is much higher for the beta emitter than for the gamma emitter.

Why is this higher dose necessary?   kill cancer

......to.....treat.....cancer.. 1

(*b*) What are the units of equivalent dose?

.... 1

Marks

7. A newborn baby is given a hearing test. A small device, containing a loudspeaker and a microphone, is placed in the baby's ear.

(*a*) A pulse of audible sound lasting 10 µs is transmitted through the loudspeaker. The sound is played at a level of 80 dB.

　(i) Give a reason why this pulse of sound does not cause damage to the baby's hearing.

　　　the Pulse time isn't big enough

1

7. (*a*) **(continued)**

(ii)   The transmitted pulse of sound makes the inner ear vibrate to produce a new sound, which is received by the microphone.

Signals from the transmitted and received sounds are viewed on an oscilloscope screen, as shown below.

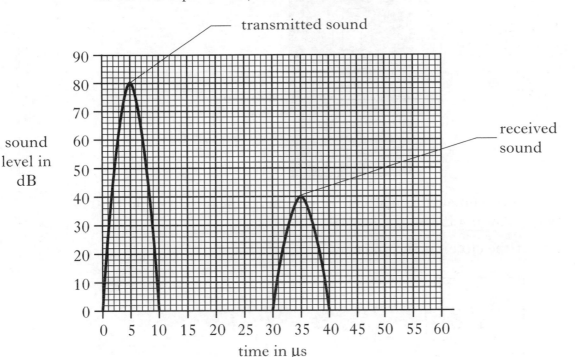

The average speed of sound inside the ear is 1500 m/s.

Calculate the distance between the device and the inner ear.

Space for working and answer

$$D = U \times t$$
$$D = 1500 \times 10$$
$$D = 15000$$

3

(iii)   Suggest a frequency that could be used for the hearing test.

.............ultrasound..   1

(*b*)   An ultrasound scan can be used to produce an image of an unborn baby.   Explain how the image of an unborn baby is formed by ultrasound.

.............the sound bounces off.............

.............the baby and creates.............

.............an image.............   2

Marks   K&U   PS

8. A high intensity LED is used as a garden light. The light turns on automatically when it becomes dark.

The light also contains a solar cell which charges a rechargeable battery during daylight hours.

(*a*) Part of the circuit is shown below.

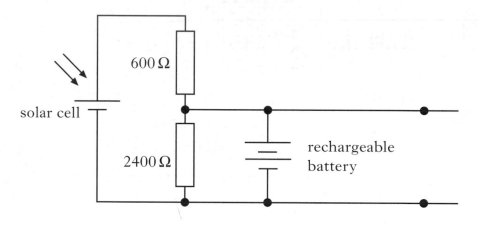

(i) State the energy transformation in a solar cell.

...... Sun to electrical   1

(ii) At a particular light level, the voltage generated by the solar cell is 1·5 V.

Calculate the voltage across the rechargeable battery at this light level.

> *Space for working and answer*
>
> V = 1.2 v

2

Marks K&U PS

8. (continued)

(*b*) The LED is switched on using the following circuit.

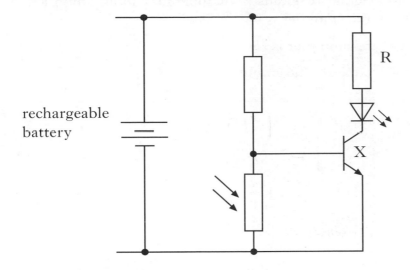

rechargeable
battery

(i) Name component X.

.... transistor 1

The graph below shows the voltage across the LDR in this circuit for different light levels.

Light level is measured in lux.

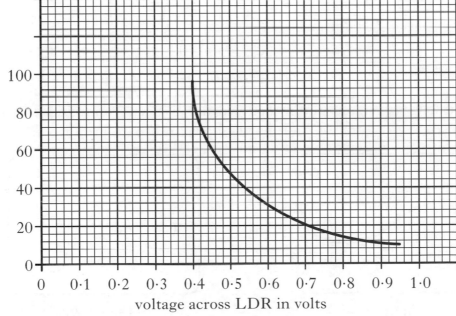

light level in lux

voltage across LDR in volts

(ii) For the LED to be lit, the voltage across the LDR must be at least 0·7 V.

What is the maximum light level for the LED to be lit?

.... 20   lux 1

(iii) Explain the purpose of resistor R.

.... to   Protect   the   LED 1

Marks | K&U | PS

9. An electronic tuner for a guitar contains a microphone and an amplifier. The output voltage from the amplifier is 9 V.

(a) The voltage gain of the amplifier is 150.

Calculate the input voltage to the amplifier.

> *Space for working and answer*
>
> 4 / 150
>
> = 0.06 v

2

(b) The tuner is used to measure the frequency of six guitar strings.

The number and frequency of each string is given in the table below.

Number of string	Frequency (Hz)
1	330·0
2	247·0
3	196·0
4	147·0
5	110·0
6	82·5

The tuner has an output socket which has been connected to an oscilloscope. The trace for string 5 is shown in Figure 1.

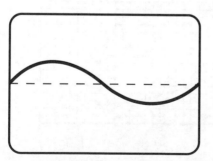

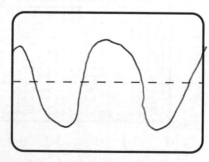

Figure 1   Figure 2

(i) The controls of the oscilloscope are **not** altered.

In Figure 2, draw the trace obtained if string 1 is played **louder** than string 5.

2

(ii) String 3 is plucked.

What is the frequency of the output signal from the amplifier?

196 Hz

1

Marks | K&U | PS

10. Cameras placed at 5 km intervals along a stretch of road are used to record the average speed of a car.

The car is travelling on a road which has a speed limit of 100 km/h. The car travels a distance of 5 km in 2·5 minutes.

(a) Does the average speed of the car stay within the speed limit? *no!*

You must justify your answer with a calculation.

Space for working and answer

$\bar{v} = D / t$

$\bar{v} = 5\,000 / 150$

$\bar{v} = 120 \quad km/h$

3

(b) At one point in the journey, the car speedometer records 90 km/h.

Explain why the average speed for the entire journey is not always the same as the speed recorded on the car speedometer.

The speedometer is recording the speed at that moment and not the over all speed

2

[Turn over

Marks | K&U | PS

11. An aeroplane on an aircraft carrier must reach a minimum speed of 70 m/s to safely take off. The mass of the aeroplane is 28 000 kg.

(*a*) The aeroplane accelerates from rest to its minimum take off speed in 2 s.

(i) Calculate the acceleration of the aeroplane.

Space for working and answer

$$a = \frac{u-v}{t} \qquad a = 35 \ m/s^2$$

$$a = \frac{70}{2}$$

2

(ii) Calculate the force required to produce this acceleration.

Space for working and answer

$$f = M \times A$$
$$f = 35 \times 28\,000$$
$$f = 980\,000$$

2

(iii) The aeroplane's engines provide a total thrust of 240 kN. An additional force is supplied by a catapult to produce the acceleration required.

Calculate the force supplied by the catapult.

Space for working and answer 740,000 N

1

Marks | K&U | PS

11. **(continued)**

(*b*) Later, the same aeroplane travelling at a speed of 65 m/s, touches down on the carrier.

(i) Calculate the kinetic energy of the aeroplane at this speed.

> *Space for working and answer*
>
> $ek = \frac{1}{2} mv^2$
>
> $ek = 28\,000 \times 65m/s \div 2$
>
> $ek = 59.82 \, mJ$

2

(ii) The graph shows the motion of the aeroplane from the point when it touches down on the carrier until it stops.

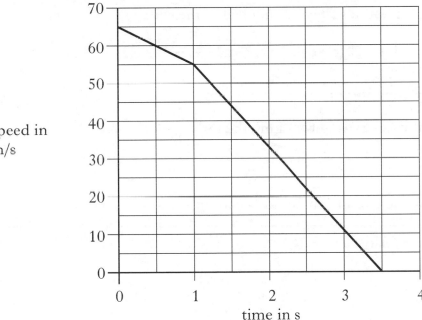

speed in m/s

time in s

Calculate the distance travelled by the aeroplane on the carrier.

> *Space for working and answer* 3.5×65
>
> $= 128.75 \, m$

2

12. The advertisement below is for a new torch.

Kinetic Torch
No batteries needed – magnet powered!
Bright white LED won't burn out!
30-40 seconds of gentle shaking produces 10-15 minutes of light!
Capacitor holds the charge generated by passing the magnet through the coil.

springs

magnet

coil

LED   movement of magnet

(a) (i) Explain how a voltage is induced in the coil.

It converts kinetic energy to electrical

(ii) What is the effect of shaking the torch faster?

More energy is gathered

(iii) Draw the circuit symbol for a capacitor.

Space for symbol

(b) When lit, the current in the LED is 20 mA.

Calculate how much charge flows through the LED in 12 minutes.

Space for working and answer   *240,000 Q*

Marks: 2, 1, 1, 2

Marks | K&U | PS

12. (continued)

(*c*) The torch produces a beam of light.

The diagram shows the LED positioned at the focus of the torch reflector.

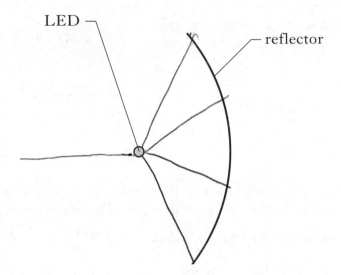

LED
reflector

Complete the diagram by drawing light rays to show how the beam of light is produced.

2

[Turn over

Marks   K&U   PS

13.   An electric kettle is used to heat 0·4 kg of water.

(*a*) The initial temperature of the water is 15 °C.

Calculate how much heat energy is required to bring this water to its boiling point of 100 °C.

> *Space for working and answer*
>
> 4180 X 75
>
> = 313500 J

3

(*b*) The automatic switch on the kettle is not working. The kettle is switched off 5 minutes after it had been switched on.

The power rating of the kettle is 2000 W.

(i)   Calculate how much electrical energy is converted into heat energy in this time.

> *Space for working and answer*
>
> 10 000 J

2

(ii) Calculate the mass of water changed into steam in this time.

> *Space for working and answer*

3

Marks | K&U | PS

14. The diagram represents the electromagnetic spectrum in order of increasing wavelength. Some of the radiations have not been named.

Electromagnetic Spectrum

Gamma rays	P	Ultraviolet	Q	Infrared	R	TV and Radio

→ increasing wavelength

(a) (i) Name radiation: P .... X Ray ....

Q .... Visible light ....

R .... Microwaves   2

(ii) Which radiation in the electromagnetic spectrum has the highest frequency?

.... TV, Radio   1

(b) Stars emit **ultraviolet** and **infrared** radiation.

Name a detector for **each** of these two radiations.

Infrared .... thermostat, thermometre ....   ①

Ultraviolet   2

[Turn over

Marks | K&U | PS

15. In June 2005, a space vehicle called Mars Lander was sent to the planet Mars.

(a) The graph shows the gravitational field strength at different heights above the surface of Mars.

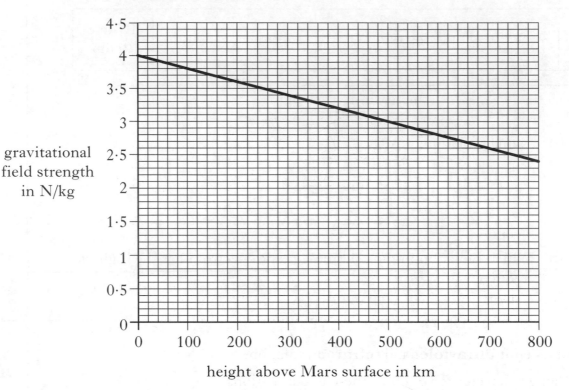

gravitational field strength in N/kg

height above Mars surface in km

(i) The Mars Lander orbited Mars at a height of 200 km above the planet's surface.

What is the value of the gravitational field strength at this height?

.... 1

(ii) The Mars Lander, of mass 530 kg, then landed.

Calculate the weight of the Mars Lander on the surface.

Space for working and answer

3

15. (continued)

(b) The Mars Lander released a rover exploration vehicle on to the surface of Mars.

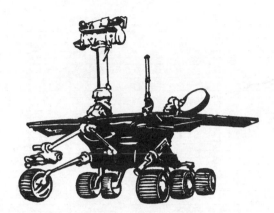

To collect data from the bottom of a large crater, the rover launched a probe horizontally at 30 m/s. The probe took 6 s to reach the bottom of the crater.

(i) Calculate the horizontal distance travelled by the probe.

> *Space for working and answer*

(ii) Calculate the vertical speed of the probe as it reached the bottom of the crater.

> *Space for working and answer*

[END OF QUESTION PAPER]

K&U | PS

YOU MAY USE THE SPACE ON THIS PAGE TO REWRITE ANY ANSWER YOU HAVE DECIDED TO CHANGE IN THE MAIN PART OF THE ANSWER BOOKLET. TAKE CARE TO WRITE IN CAREFULLY THE APPROPRIATE QUESTION NUMBER.

[BLANK PAGE]

FOR OFFICIAL USE

C

	K & U	PS

Total Marks

3220/402

NATIONAL
QUALIFICATIONS
2008

FRIDAY, 23 MAY
10.50 AM – 12.35 PM

PHYSICS
STANDARD GRADE
Credit Level

Fill in these boxes and read what is printed below.

Full name of centre

Town

Forename(s)

Surname

Date of birth
Day Month Year   Scottish candidate number   Number of seat

Reference may be made to the Physics Data Booklet.

1 All questions should be answered.

2 The questions may be answered in any order but all answers must be written clearly and legibly in this book.

3 Write your answer where indicated by the question or in the space provided after the question.

4 If you change your mind about your answer you may score it out and rewrite it in the space provided at the end of the answer book.

5 Before leaving the examination room you must give this book to the invigilator. If you do not, you may lose all the marks for this paper.

6 Any necessary data will be found in the **data sheet** on page three.

7 Care should be taken to give an appropriate number of significant figures in the final answers to questions.

[BLANK PAGE]

DATA SHEET

Speed of light in materials

Material	Speed in m/s
Air	$3{\cdot}0 \times 10^8$
Carbon dioxide	$3{\cdot}0 \times 10^8$
Diamond	$1{\cdot}2 \times 10^8$
Glass	$2{\cdot}0 \times 10^8$
Glycerol	$2{\cdot}1 \times 10^8$
Water	$2{\cdot}3 \times 10^8$

Speed of sound in materials

Material	Speed in m/s
Aluminium	5200
Air	340
Bone	4100
Carbon dioxide	270
Glycerol	1900
Muscle	1600
Steel	5200
Tissue	1500
Water	1500

Gravitational field strengths

	Gravitational field strength on the surface in N/kg
Earth	10
Jupiter	26
Mars	4
Mercury	4
Moon	1·6
Neptune	12
Saturn	11
Sun	270
Venus	9

Specific heat capacity of materials

Material	Specific heat capacity in J/kg °C
Alcohol	2350
Aluminium	902
Copper	386
Glass	500
Glycerol	2400
Ice	2100
Lead	128
Silica	1033
Water	4180

Specific latent heat of fusion of materials

Material	Specific latent heat of fusion in J/kg
Alcohol	$0{\cdot}99 \times 10^5$
Aluminium	$3{\cdot}95 \times 10^5$
Carbon dioxide	$1{\cdot}80 \times 10^5$
Copper	$2{\cdot}05 \times 10^5$
Glycerol	$1{\cdot}81 \times 10^5$
Lead	$0{\cdot}25 \times 10^5$
Water	$3{\cdot}34 \times 10^5$

Melting and boiling points of materials

Material	Melting point in °C	Boiling point in °C
Alcohol	−98	65
Aluminium	660	2470
Copper	1077	2567
Glycerol	18	290
Lead	328	1737
Turpentine	−10	156

Specific latent heat of vaporisation of materials

Material	Specific latent heat of vaporisation in J/kg
Alcohol	$11{\cdot}2 \times 10^5$
Carbon dioxide	$3{\cdot}77 \times 10^5$
Glycerol	$8{\cdot}30 \times 10^5$
Turpentine	$2{\cdot}90 \times 10^5$
Water	$22{\cdot}6 \times 10^5$

SI Prefixes and Multiplication Factors

Prefix	Symbol	Factor	
giga	G	1 000 000 000	$= 10^9$
mega	M	1 000 000	$= 10^6$
kilo	k	1000	$= 10^3$
milli	m	0·001	$= 10^{-3}$
micro	μ	0·000 001	$= 10^{-6}$
nano	n	0·000 000 001	$= 10^{-9}$

DO NOT
WRITE IN
THIS
MARGIN

K&U PS

Marks

1. A high definition television picture has 1080 lines and there are 25 pictures produced each second.

(a) (i) Calculate how long it takes to produce one picture on the screen.

Space for working and answer

1 ÷ 25 = 0.04 s

1

(ii) Explain why a continuous moving picture is seen on the television screen and not 25 individual pictures each second.

human eye sees ~~ret~~ 24 frames per second.

①

2

(b) The television picture is in colour.

(i) Which **two** colours are used to produce magenta on the screen?

blue and red

1

(ii) Due to a fault, the colour yellow appears as orange on the screen. Which colour should be reduced in brightness to correct this problem?

reduce red

1

OFFICIAL SQA PAST PAPERS   37   CREDIT PHYSICS 2008

DO NOT
WRITE IN
THIS
MARGIN

K&U | PS

Marks

2. A television company is making a programme in China.

Britain receives television pictures live from China. The television signals are transmitted using microwaves. The microwave signals travel from China **via** a satellite, which is in a geostationary orbit.

(*a*) State what is meant by a geostationary orbit.

......~~...~~... it takes 24 hours to circle the earth   (1)

(*b*) The diagram shows the position of the transmitter and receiver. Complete the diagram to show the path of the microwave signals **from** China **to** Britain.

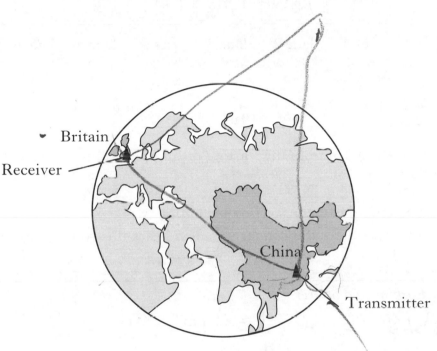

2

(*c*) The frequency of the microwave signals being used for transmission is 8 GHz.

(i) What is the speed of the microwaves?

......3×10^8 m/s......   (1)

(ii) Calculate the wavelength of these microwaves.

Space for working and answer

$\lambda = v/f$

$\lambda = 8 \times 10^6 / 3 \times 10^8$

$\lambda = 3.75 \times 10^{13}$

2

Marks

3. In a sprint race at a school sports day, the runners start when they hear the sound of the starting pistol. An electronic timer is also started when the pistol is fired into the air.

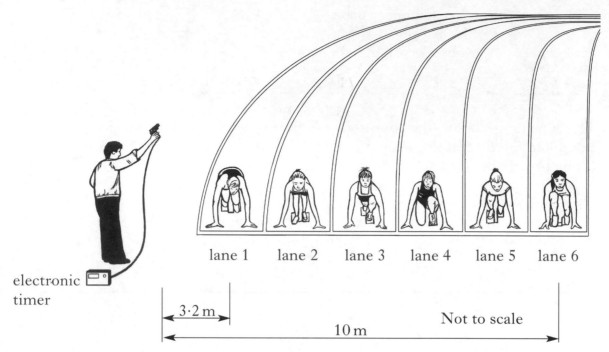

electronic timer

lane 1   lane 2   lane 3   lane 4   lane 5   lane 6

3·2 m

Not to scale

10 m

The runner in lane 1 is 3·2 m from the starting pistol. The runner in lane 6 is 10 m from the starting pistol.

(a) The runner in lane 1 hears the starting pistol first.

Calculate how much later the runner in lane 6 hears this sound after the runner in lane 1.

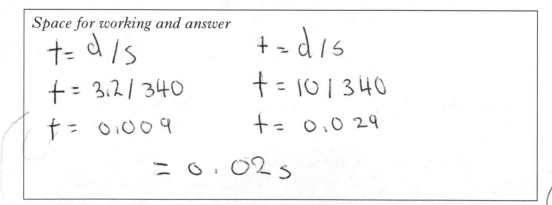

Space for working and answer

$t = d/s$ $t = d/s$

$t = 3.2/340$ $t = 10/340$

$t = 0.009$ $t = 0.029$

$= 0.02 s$

3

Marks

3. **(continued)**

(*b*) A sensor detects each runner crossing the finishing line to record their time.

The table gives information about the race.

Place	Lane	Time (s)
1st	1	13·11
2nd	6	13·12
3rd	3	13·21

Using your answer to part (*a*), explain why the runner in lane 6 should have been awarded first place.

> *Space for working and answer*
>
> 0·02 seconds should have been subtracted from his time

2

(*c*) One runner of mass 60 kg has a speed of 9 m/s when crossing the finishing line.

Calculate the kinetic energy of the runner at this point.

> *Space for working and answer*
>
> $ek = \frac{1}{2} mv^2$
>
> $ek = 60 \times 9^2 \div 2$
>
> $ek = 2430 \text{ J}$

2

[Turn over

DO NOT
WRITE IN
THIS
MARGIN

K&U | PS

Marks

4. A student has four resistors labelled A, B, C and D. The student sets up Circuit 1 to identify the value of each resistor.

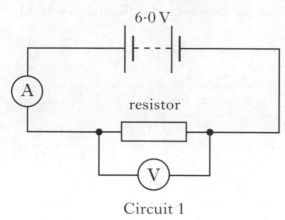

6·0 V

A

resistor

V

Circuit 1

Each resistor is placed in the circuit in turn and the following results are obtained.

Resistor	Voltage across resistor (V)	Current (A)
A	6·0	0·017
B	6·0	0·027
C	6·0	0·050
D	6·0	0·033

(a) (i) Show, **by calculation**, which of the resistors has a value of $120\,\Omega$.

Space for working and answer

R = V / I

R = 6 / 0·05

R = 120 Ω

3

IT IS RESISTOR C

DO NOT
WRITE IN
THIS
MARGIN

K&U | PS

Marks

4. **(a)** **(continued)**

(ii) The student then sets up Circuit 2 to measure the resistance of each resistor.

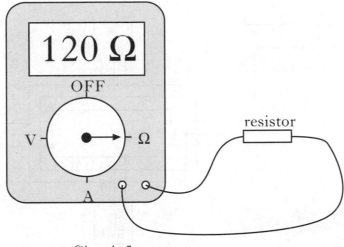

resistor

Circuit 2

State **one** advantage of using Circuit 2 to measure the resistance compared to using Circuit 1.

it's ~~a~~ a single instrument
that does the job of many

1

(b) The resistances of the other three resistors are 180 Ω, 220 Ω and 360 Ω. The student connects all four resistors in series.

Calculate the total resistance.

Space for working and answer

120 + 180 + 220 + 360

= 880 Ω

2

[Turn over

K&U | PS

Marks

5. The diagram shows three household circuits connected to a consumer unit.

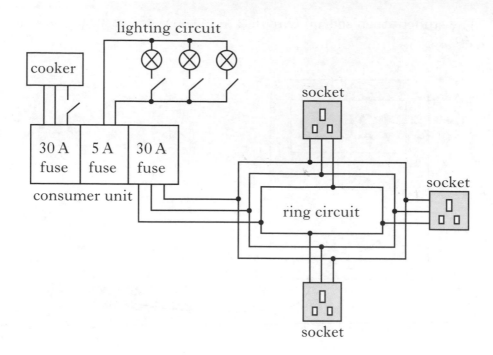

lighting circuit

cooker

30 A fuse   5 A fuse   30 A fuse

consumer unit

socket

ring circuit

socket

socket

(*a*) (i) State **one** advantage of a ring circuit.

.......less.......current.. ①

(ii) State the value of mains voltage.

.......230 V.. ①

(*b*) Each of the lamps in the lighting circuit has a power rating of 100 W. One of the lamps is switched on.

(i) Calculate the current in the lamp.

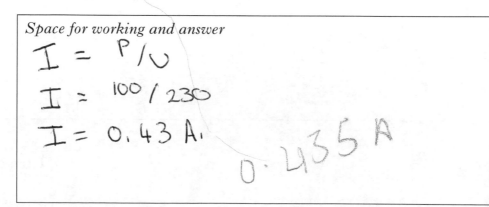

Space for working and answer

$I = P/U$

$I = 100/230$

$I = 0.43$ A.

0·435 A

②

DO NOT
WRITE IN
THIS
MARGIN

K&U | PS

Marks

5. (b) (continued)

(ii) Explain why a house with twenty 100 W lamps requires two separate lighting circuits.

in case the current is too high

un each branch

2

[Turn over

DO NOT
WRITE IN
THIS
MARGIN

Marks

6. A short-sighted person has difficulty seeing the picture on a cinema screen.

Figure 1 shows rays of light from the screen entering an eye of the person until the rays reach the retina.

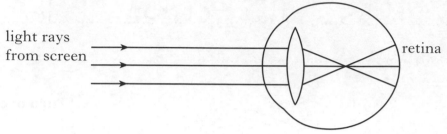

Figure 1

(*a*) (i) In the dotted box in Figure 2, draw the shape of lens that would correct this eye defect.

1

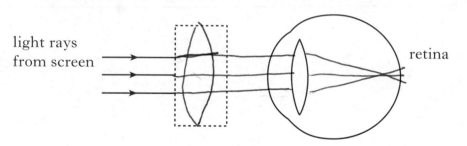

Figure 2

(ii) In Figure 2, complete the path of the rays of light from this lens until they reach the retina.

2

6. **(continued)**

(b) Doctors can use an endoscope to examine internal organs of a patient. The endoscope has two separate bundles of optical fibres that are flexible.

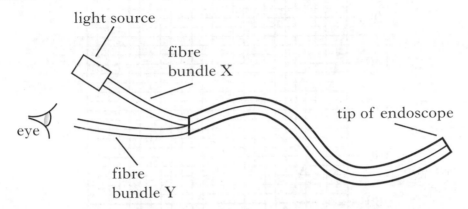

A section of optical fibre used in the endoscope is shown below.

(i) Complete the diagram to show how light is transmitted along the optical fibre.

(ii) Explain the purpose of each bundle of optical fibres in the endoscope.

Fibre bundle X .....to....beam....light...
....into....the....body......

Fibre bundle Y .....So......the....doctor...
...can....see....into....the....body....

(iii) The tip of the endoscope that is inside the patient is designed to be very flexible. Suggest **one** reason for this.
....if....it....was....brittle....it....would...
....hurt.

[Turn over

Marks

7. A hospital technician is working with a radioactive source. The graph shows the activity of the source over a period of time.

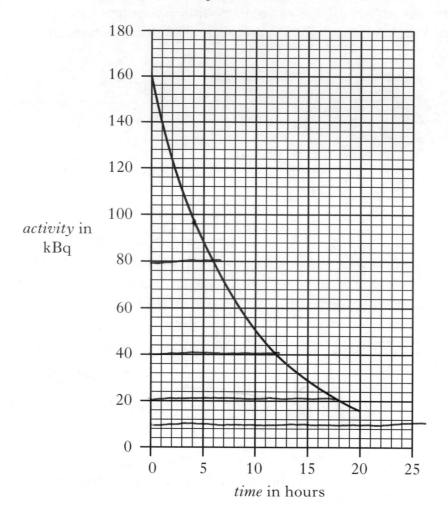

activity in
kBq

time in hours

(*a*) (i) State what is meant by the term *half-life*.

time taken for activity to divide by two   ①

(ii) Use information from the graph to calculate the half-life of the radioactive source.

Space for working and answer

6 hours

1

K&U   PS

Marks

7. **(a)** **(continued)**

(iii)   The initial activity of the source is 160 kBq.

Calculate the activity, in kBq, of the radioactive source after four half-lives.

Space for working and answer

90 kBq

10

1

(b)   As a safety precaution the technician wears a film badge when working with radioactive sources. The film badge contains photographic film. Light cannot enter the badge.

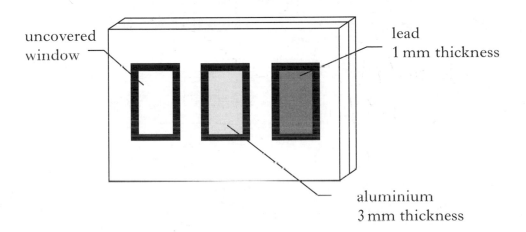

uncovered window

lead
1 mm thickness

aluminium
3 mm thickness

Describe how the film badge indicates the **type** and **amount** of radiation received.

....

....

....

....

2

[Turn over

Marks

8. A torch contains five identical LEDs connected to a 3·0 V battery as shown.

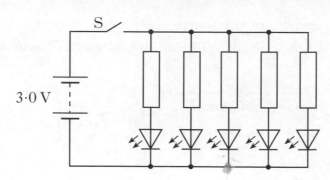

(*a*) State the purpose of the resistor connected in series with each LED.

...it protects the led from current... ① **1**

(*b*) When lit, each LED operates at a voltage of 1·8 V and a current of 30 mA.

(i) Calculate the value of the resistor in series with each LED.

> Space for working and answer
>
> R = V/I
>
> R = 1·8/0·03
>
> R = 60 Ω
>
> 40 ~

②
⊘

3

(ii) Calculate the total current from the supply when all five LEDs are lit.

> Space for working and answer
>
> 5 X 0·03 = 0·15 m

① **1**

Marks

K&U | PS

8. **(b) (continued)**

(iii) Calculate the power supplied by the battery when all five LEDs are lit.

> *Space for working and answer*
>
> $P = I^2 R$
>
> $P = 0.16^2 \times 60$
>
> $P = 1.35 \ W$

2

(c) State **one** advantage of using five LEDs rather than a single filament lamp in the torch.

...... less energy consumed **1**

[Turn over

Marks

9. An electronic device produces a changing light pattern when it detects music, but only when it is in the dark.

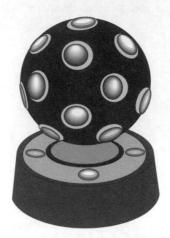

The device contains the logic circuit shown.

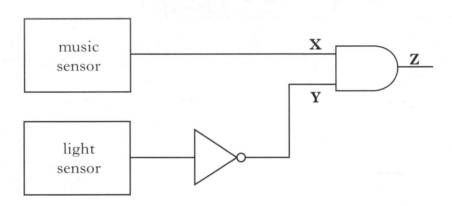

The music sensor produces logic 1 when the music is on and logic 0 when the music is off.

The light sensor produces logic 1 when it detects light and logic 0 when it is dark.

(a) (i) Suggest a suitable input device for the light sensor.

.... IDR   1

(ii) Complete the truth table for the logic levels at points **X**, **Y** and **Z** in the circuit.

Music	*Light level*	**X**	**Y**	**Z**
off	dark	0	1	0
off	light	0	0	0
on	dark	1	1	1
on	light	1	0	0

3

Marks

9. **(continued)**

(b) The device detects music from a CD player. The CD player contains an amplifier that produces an output voltage of 5·6 V when connected to a loudspeaker of resistance 3·2 Ω.

(i) Calculate the output power of the amplifier.

Space for working and answer

$$P = V \times R$$
$$P = 5.6 \times 3.2$$
$$P = 17.92 \text{ W}$$

2

(ii) The input power to the amplifier is 4·9 mW.

Calculate the power gain of the amplifier.

Space for working and answer

2

(iii) One particular signal from the CD to the amplifier has a frequency of 170 Hz.

What is the frequency of the output signal from the amplifier?

.... 170 ....

1

[Turn over

10. A railway train travels uphill between two stations.

Information about the train and its journey is given below.

average speed of train	5 m/s
time for journey	150 s
power of train	120 kW
mass of train plus passengers	20 000 kg

(*a*) Calculate the energy used by the train during the journey.

Space for working and answer

$$e_k = \tfrac{1}{2} m1v^2$$

$$e_k = \tfrac{1}{2} \, 20{,}000 / 5^2$$

$$e_k = 1.8 \times 10^7)$$

2

DO NOT
WRITE IN
THIS
MARGIN

K&U PS

Marks

10. (continued)

(b) Calculate the height gained by the train during the journey.

> *Space for working and answer*
>
> 90 m
>
> P

2

(c) Suggest why the actual height gained by the train is less than the value calculated in part (b).

energy is lost through other things.

1

[Turn over

11. A windsurfer takes part in a race. The windsurfer takes 120 seconds to complete the race. The total mass of the windsurfer and the board is 90 kg.

The graph shows how the speed of the windsurfer and board changes with time during part of the race.

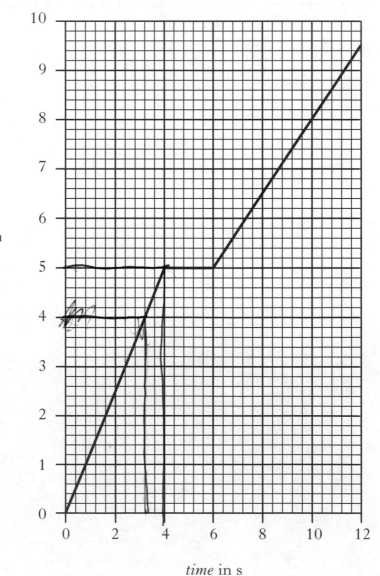

speed in m/s

time in s

Marks

11. (continued)

(*a*) (i) Calculate the acceleration of the windsurfer and board during the first 4 s of the race.

> *Space for working and answer*
>
> $a = \dfrac{v-u}{t}$
>
> $a = \dfrac{5}{4}$
>
> $a = 1.25 \text{ m/s}^2$

2

(ii) Calculate the unbalanced force causing this acceleration.

> *Space for working and answer*
>
> $f = m \times A$
>
> $f = 90 \times 1.25$
>
> $f = 112.5 \text{ N}$

2

(*b*) Calculate the total distance travelled by the windsurfer during the 12 s time interval shown on the graph.

> *Space for working and answer*
>
> $d = s \times t$
>
> $d = 5 \times 12$
>
> $d = 60 \text{ m}$

1

2

(*c*) What can be said about the horizontal forces acting on the windsurfer between 4 s and 6 s?

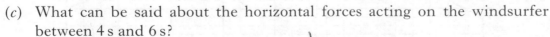 they are balanced

1

[Turn over

DO NOT
WRITE IN
THIS
MARGIN

| K&U | PS |

12. An underwater generator is designed to produce electricity from water currents in the sea.

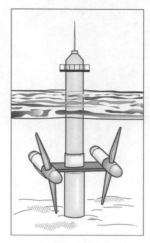

The output power of the generator depends on the speed of the water current as shown in Graph 1.

Graph 1

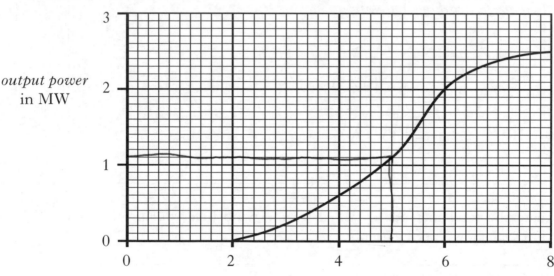

speed of water current in m/s

The speed of the water current is recorded at different times of the day shown in Graph 2.

Graph 2

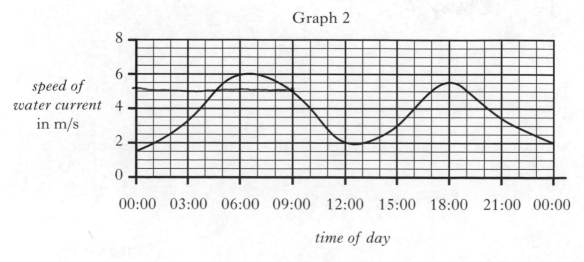

time of day

Marks

12. (continued)

(a) (i) State the output power of the generator at 09:00.

.......1.1 ~~MW~~ MW......... 1

(ii) State **one** disadvantage of using this type of generator.

.......currents aren't always strong... 1

(b) The voltage produced by the generator is stepped-up by a transformer.

At one point in the day the electrical current in the primary coils of the transformer is 900 A and the voltage is 2000 V.

The transformer is 96% efficient.

(i) Calculate the output power of the transformer at this time.

> Space for working and answer
>
> 900 × 2000 ÷ 100 × 96
>
> = 1 728 000 N

3

(ii) State **one** reason why a transformer is not 100% efficient.

.......energy is lost through other means... 1

[Turn over

12. (continued)

(c) Three different types of electrical generator, X, Y and Z are tested in a special tank with a current of water as shown to find out the efficiency of each generator.

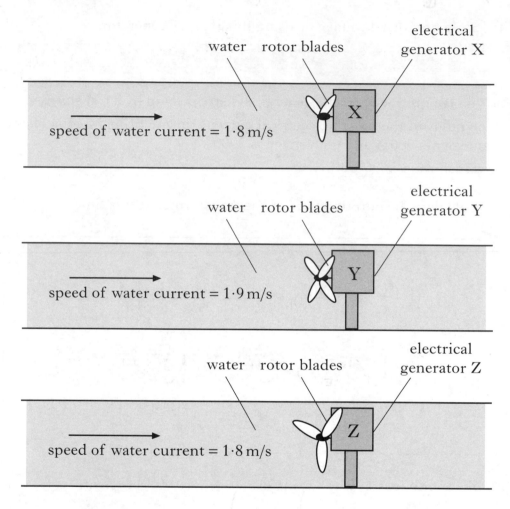

Give **two** reasons why this is not a fair test.

Speed isn't a constant variable

Marks

1

Marks

13. In the reactor of a nuclear power station, neutrons split uranium nuclei to produce heat in what is known as a "chain reaction".

   (a) Explain what is meant by the term "chain reaction".

   an reaction that causes a
   serious ot other events   2

   (b) In the nuclear power station, 1 kg of uranium fuel produces 4 200 000 MJ of heat. In a coal-fired power station 1 kg of coal produces 28 MJ of heat.

   Calculate how many kilograms of coal are required to produce the same amount of heat as 1 kg of uranium.

   > *Space for working and answer*
   >
   > 4200, 000 / 28
   >
   > = 150, 000 kg

   1

   (c) A power station uses an a.c. generator to convert kinetic energy from a turbine into electrical energy. A diagram of an a.c. generator is shown.

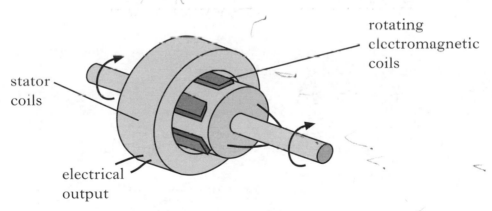

   stator coils

   rotating electromagnetic coils

   electrical output

   (i) Explain how the a.c. generator works.

   it flows both ways   2

   (ii) State **two** changes that can be made to the generator to increase the output power.

   Change 1: ....

   Change 2:   2

K&U | PS

Marks

14. A team of astronomers observes a star 200 light-years away.

(a) State what is meant by the term "light-year".

.......~~Place~~ how far light travels in a year....... 1

(b) Images of the star are taken with three different types of telescope as shown.

  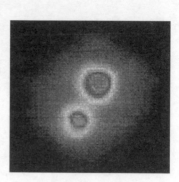

Telescope A   Telescope B   Telescope C
visible light   infrared   X-ray

(i) Explain why different types of telescope are used to detect signals from space.

.......different signals give off.......
.......different Radiation....... 2

(ii) Place the telescopes in order of the increasing wavelength of the radiation which they detect.

.......C B A....... 1

(iii) State a detector that could be used in telescope C.

.......Film....... 1

(c) Telescope A is a refracting telescope with an objective lens of focal length 400 mm and diameter 80 mm.

(i) Calculate the power of the objective lens.

Space for working and answer

$P = \frac{1}{fi}$ $P = 0.0125 \ bq$

$P = \frac{1}{80}$

2

DO NOT WRITE IN THIS MARGIN

K&U	PS

Marks

14. (*c*) (continued)

(ii) One of the astronomers suggests replacing the objective lens in this telescope with one of larger diameter.

State an advantage of doing this.

......larger focus...... **1**

[Turn over for Question 15 on *Page thirty*

58/62

68/100

Marks | K&U | PS

15. (a) A spacecraft is used to transport astronauts and equipment to a space station. On its return from space the spacecraft must re-enter the Earth's atmosphere. The spacecraft has a heat shield made from special silica tiles to prevent the inside from becoming too hot.

(i) Why does the spacecraft increase in temperature when it re-enters the atmosphere?

~~friction~~ friction 1

(ii) The mass of the heat shield is $3 \cdot 5 \times 10^3$ kg and the gain in heat energy of the silica tiles is $4 \cdot 7$ GJ.

Calculate the increase in temperature of the silica tiles.

Space for working and answer   1300 – 1500°

3

(iii) Explain why the actual temperature rise of the silica tiles is less than the value calculated in (a)(ii).

energy is lost in sound 1

(b) When a piece of equipment was loaded on to the spacecraft on Earth, two people were required to lift it.

One person was able to lift the same piece of equipment in the Space Station.

Explain why one person was able to lift the equipment in the Space Station.

It's weight is lost 1

[END OF QUESTION PAPER]

YOU MAY USE THE SPACE ON THIS PAGE TO REWRITE ANY ANSWER
YOU HAVE DECIDED TO CHANGE IN THE MAIN PART OF THE ANSWER
BOOKLET. TAKE CARE TO WRITE IN CAREFULLY THE APPROPRIATE
QUESTION NUMBER.

[BLANK PAGE]

[BLANK PAGE]

FOR OFFICIAL USE

C

K&U   PS

3220/402

NATIONAL
QUALIFICATIONS
2009

TUESDAY, 26 MAY
10.50 AM – 12.35 PM

PHYSICS
STANDARD GRADE
Credit Level

Fill in these boxes and read what is printed below.

Full name of centre

Town

Forename(s)

Surname

Date of birth

Day   Month   Year   Scottish candidate number

Number of seat

Reference may be made to the Physics Data Booklet.

1 All questions should be answered.

2 The questions may be answered in any order but all answers must be written clearly and legibly in this book.

3 Write your answer where indicated by the question or in the space provided after the question.

4 If you change your mind about your answer you may score it out and rewrite it in the space provided at the end of the answer book.

5 If you use the additional space at the end of the answer book for answering any questions, you **must** write the correct question number beside each answer.

6 Before leaving the examination room you must give this book to the invigilator. If you do not, you may lose all the marks for this paper.

7 Any necessary data will be found in the **data sheet** on page three.

8 Care should be taken to give an appropriate number of significant figures in the final answers to questions.

Use **blue** or **black ink**. Pencil may be used for graphs and diagrams only.

[BLANK PAGE]

DATA SHEET

Speed of light in materials

Material	Speed in m/s
Air	$3 \cdot 0 \times 10^8$
Carbon dioxide	$3 \cdot 0 \times 10^8$
Diamond	$1 \cdot 2 \times 10^8$
Glass	$2 \cdot 0 \times 10^8$
Glycerol	$2 \cdot 1 \times 10^8$
Water	$2 \cdot 3 \times 10^8$

Speed of sound in materials

Material	Speed in m/s
Aluminium	5200
Air	340
Bone	4100
Carbon dioxide	270
Glycerol	1900
Muscle	1600
Steel	5200
Tissue	1500
Water	1500

Gravitational field strengths

	Gravitational field strength on the surface in N/kg
Earth	10
Jupiter	26
Mars	4
Mercury	4
Moon	1·6
Neptune	12
Saturn	11
Sun	270
Venus	9

Specific heat capacity of materials

Material	Specific heat capacity in J/kg °C
Alcohol	2350
Aluminium	902
Copper	386
Glass	500
Glycerol	2400
Ice	2100
Lead	128
Silica	1033
Water	4180

Specific latent heat of fusion of materials

Material	Specific latent heat of fusion in J/kg
Alcohol	$0 \cdot 99 \times 10^5$
Aluminium	$3 \cdot 95 \times 10^5$
Carbon dioxide	$1 \cdot 80 \times 10^5$
Copper	$2 \cdot 05 \times 10^5$
Glycerol	$1 \cdot 81 \times 10^5$
Lead	$0 \cdot 25 \times 10^5$
Water	$3 \cdot 34 \times 10^5$

Melting and boiling points of materials

Material	Melting point in °C	Boiling point in °C
Alcohol	−98	65
Aluminium	660	2470
Copper	1077	2567
Glycerol	18	290
Lead	328	1737
Turpentine	−10	156

Specific latent heat of vaporisation of materials

Material	Specific latent heat of vaporisation in J/kg
Alcohol	$11 \cdot 2 \times 10^5$
Carbon dioxide	$3 \cdot 77 \times 10^5$
Glycerol	$8 \cdot 30 \times 10^5$
Turpentine	$2 \cdot 90 \times 10^5$
Water	$22 \cdot 6 \times 10^5$

SI Prefixes and Multiplication Factors

Prefix	Symbol	Factor	
giga	G	1 000 000 000	$= 10^9$
mega	M	1 000 000	$= 10^6$
kilo	k	1000	$= 10^3$
milli	m	0·001	$= 10^{-3}$
micro	μ	0·000 001	$= 10^{-6}$
nano	n	0·000 000 001	$= 10^{-9}$

Marks

1. A laptop computer uses a radio signal to transfer information to a base station. The base station is connected by optical fibres to a telephone exchange.

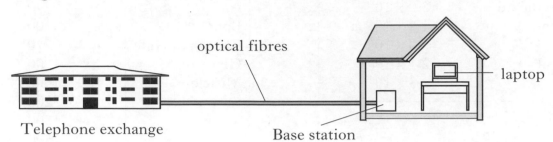

optical fibres

laptop

Telephone exchange

Base station

(a) The frequency of the radio signal is 5 GHz.

   (i) State the speed of the radio signal.

   3×10^8 ~~3×10^8~~   ~~3×10^{10} m/s~~ 340 m/s   **1**

   (ii) Calculate the wavelength of the radio signal.

   Space for working and answer

   $\lambda = 3 \times 10^8 / 5 \times 10^9$

   $\lambda = 0.06 \, m$

   $\lambda = $ ~~...~~

   2

(b) The telephone exchange is 40 km away from the base station.

   Calculate the time taken for the signal to travel along the **glass** optical fibre from the base station to the local telephone exchange.

   Space for working and answer

   $T = D/s$

   $T = 40,000 / 2 \times 10^8$

   $T = 0.0002 \, s$

   3

(c) Copper wire can also be used to transfer information between the base station and the telephone exchange.

   State **one** advantage of using optical fibres compared to copper wire.

   More packets of information   **1**

Marks

2. A ship is carrying out a survey of the sea bed using ultrasound waves.

When stationary, the ship transmits and receives pulses of ultrasound waves. The transmitted ultrasound waves have a frequency of 30 kHz.

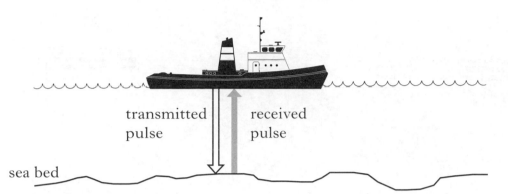

transmitted   received
pulse   pulse

sea bed

(*a*) What is meant by ultrasound?

a sound that is higher than the
hearable frequency   1

(*b*) What is the speed of ultrasound waves in water?

1500 m/s   1

(*c*) One pulse of ultrasound is received back at the ship 0·36 s after being transmitted.

Calculate the depth of the sea bed.

Space for working and answer

Distance

D = s × t

D = 1500 × 0·36 ÷ 2

D = 270 m   1

3

[Turn over

Marks

3. A rock concert is being held at Hampden Stadium. The concert is being filmed and is displayed on a large screen above the stage. This allows the band to be seen clearly by people at the back of the stadium.

(a) The people at the back of the stadium, watching the screen, notice that there is a time delay between seeing the drummer hitting the drums and hearing the sound.

Explain why there is a time delay.

.... the movement or light

travels faster than the sound

1

(b) The concert is also being broadcast live on radio and television.

The audio signal is combined with a radio carrier wave to produce a modulated radio signal.

The audio signal and the modulated radio signal are shown below.

Draw the radio carrier wave in the space provided.

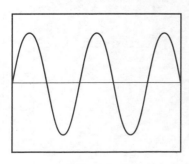 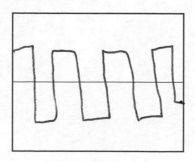 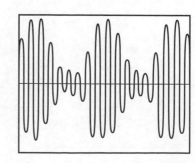

audio signal   radio carrier wave   modulated radio signal

2

3. (continued)

(c) An electric guitar used in the concert is connected to an amplifier.

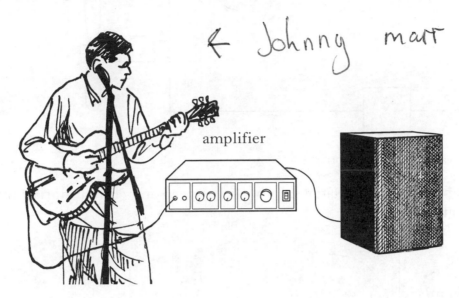

amplifier

The input power of the signal from the guitar to the amplifier is 30 mW.
The output of the amplifier is connected to a loudspeaker.
The amplifier has a power gain of 25 000.

Calculate the output power delivered to the loudspeaker.

Space for working and answer

2

[Turn over

4. A car fan uses a battery powered electric motor. The diagram below shows the apparatus used to investigate the effect of current on the speed of the electric motor.

Marks

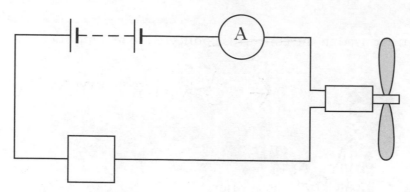

variable speed control

(a) The graph shows the relationship between speed and current during the investigation.

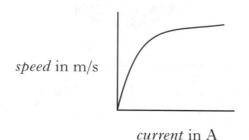

speed in m/s

current in A

(i) The current is changed using the variable speed control.

What happens to the current when the resistance of the variable speed controller is reduced?

it is ~~reduced~~ increased   ①

(ii) The settings of the variable speed control use different combinations of **identical** resistors, as shown.

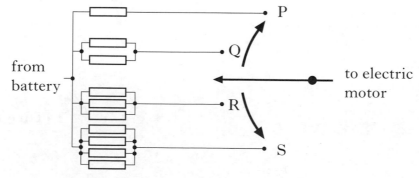

(A) To which position should the variable speed control be set to achieve maximum speed?

S   ①

(B) Justify your answer.

it is the Path of least resistance   ①

4. **(continued)**

Marks

(b) The electric motor is shown below.

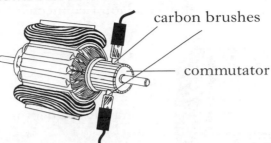

carbon brushes

commutator

(i) Explain the purpose of the commutator.

it makes the motor go the right direction

1

(ii) Why are the brushes made of carbon rather than metal wire?

less friction

1

(c) When a wire carrying a current is placed in a magnetic field, a force is produced on the wire. The diagram shows the direction of the force for a particular situation.

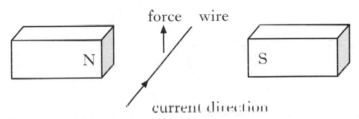

force   wire

N

S

current direction

(i) A simplified diagram of an electric motor is shown below. Indicate on the diagram the direction of the force on the wire at point X and point Y.

1

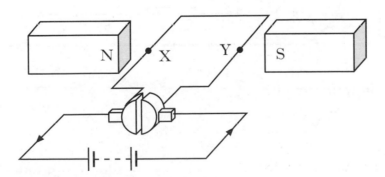

N   X   Y   S

(ii) State **one** way in which the direction of rotation of the motor could be reversed.

Switch the magnets Position

1

Marks

5. A householder plugs a home entertainment centre, a hi-fi, a games console and an electric fire into a multiway adaptor connected to the mains.

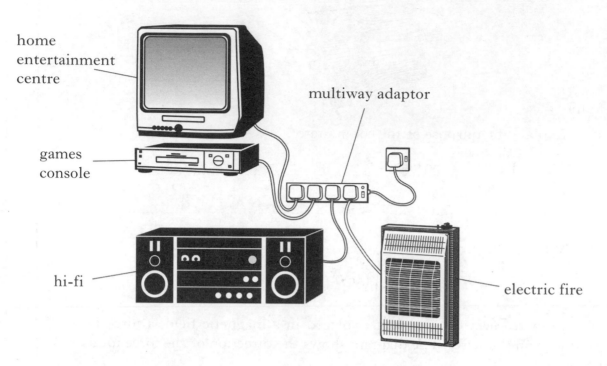

home entertainment centre

games console

hi-fi

multiway adaptor

electric fire

The wiring in the electric fire is found to be faulty. The circuit is shown below.

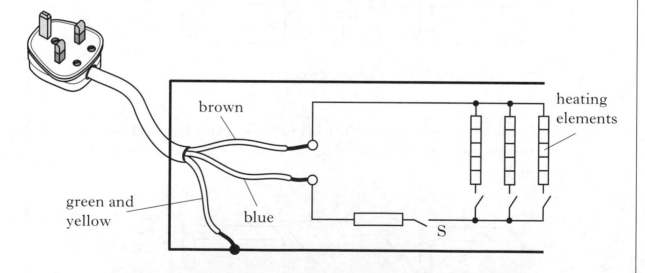

brown

green and yellow

blue

S

heating elements

(*a*) What is the fault in the circuit?

the switches are on the wrong side

1

Marks

5.   (continued)

(b) The householder goes on holiday for 14 days.

The electric fire is unplugged.

All the other appliances are left on standby.

On standby, these appliances operate at 9·0% of their power rating listed in the table.

Appliance	Power rating (W)
home entertainment centre	350
hi-fi	150
games console	300
electric fire	2080

(i) Calculate the total power consumption, in watts, of all the appliances left **on standby**.

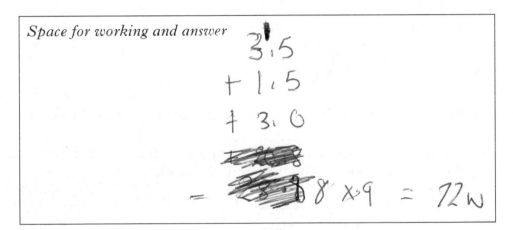

Space for working and answer

$$3.5$$
$$+ 1.5$$
$$+ 3.0$$
$$= 8 \times 9 = 72w$$

2

(ii) Calculate the number of kilowatt-hours used by these appliances during the 14 days on standby.

Space for working and answer

2

[Turn over

Marks

6. In a physics laboratory, a student wants to find the focal length of a convex lens. The student is given a sheet of white paper, a metre stick and a lens.

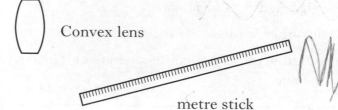

paper

Convex lens

metre stick

(a) Explain how the student could measure the focal length of the lens using this equipment.

Shine a light image onto the Paper until it is clear then measure the distance

2

(b) Refraction of light occurs in lenses.

What is meant by the term refraction?

When light bends through an object.

2

(c) The following diagram shows a ray of light entering a glass block.

(i) Complete the diagram to show the path of the ray of light through the block and after it emerges from the block.

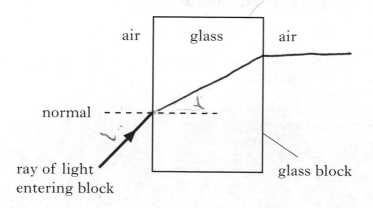

air　glass　air

normal

ray of light
entering block

glass block

2

(ii) On your diagram indicate an angle of refraction, **r**.

1

Marks

7. Students observe an experiment with radioactive sources. The radiation is measured using a detector and counter. The background count rate is measured.

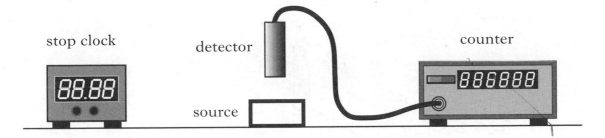

Different absorbing materials are then placed, in turn, between source and detector and readings for each material are recorded. This is repeated for each source. The results are shown in the table.

| Source | Corrected Count Rate (Counts per minute) | | | |
	No absorbing material	Paper	2 cm of Aluminium	2 cm of Lead
A	480	480	480	200
B	720	300	300	180
C	600	580	0	0

One source emits beta radiation only, one emits gamma only and one emits both alpha and gamma radiation.

(a) Complete the following table to identify the source.

Type of radiation	Source
beta only	C
both alpha and gamma	b

1

(b) One source has a half-life of 30 minutes.
The source has an initial activity of 18 000 Bq.
Calculate its activity after 2 hours.

Space for working and answer

2250 B9

1125 B9

2

Marks

8. A digital camera is used to take pictures. When switched on, the flash on a digital camera requires some time before it is ready to operate. When ready, a green LED is illuminated.

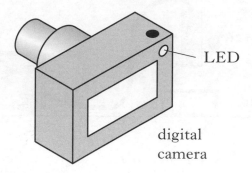

LED

digital
camera

The part of the circuit used to control the LED is shown below. The voltage at point X is initially 0 V.

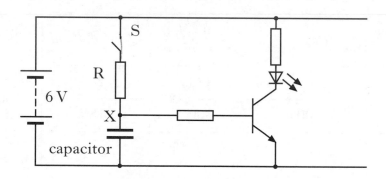

(a) Describe what happens to the voltage at point X when switch S is closed.

............It....hits....six.....volts................................. 1

(b) The camera manufacturer wants to change the time taken for the flash to be ready to operate.

State **two** changes which could be made to the above circuit so that the time for the green LED to come on is **reduced**.

...........Remove....or....adjust....the............
.........capacitor.. 2

DO NOT
WRITE IN
THIS
MARGIN

K&U | PS

Marks

8.   (continued)

(c)   The camera flash is designed to operate under dim lighting conditions. Another part of the circuit for the camera flash is shown below. The flash only operates when a minimum voltage of 0·7 V occurs across the LDR.

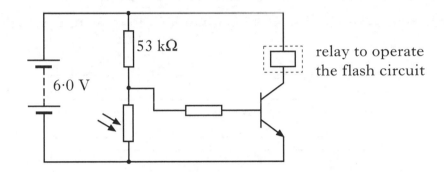

(i)   Calculate the voltage across the 53 kΩ resistor when the voltage across the LDR is 0·7 V.

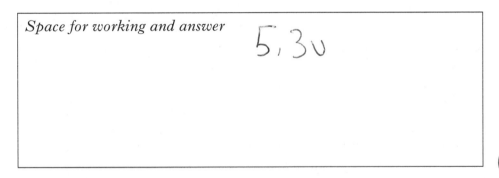

Space for working and answer

5·3υ

1

(ii)   Calculate the **minimum** resistance of the LDR that allows the flash to operate in dim conditions.

Space for working and answer

0·7 υ

7000 Ω

2

[Turn over

Marks

9. A remote gas sensing system detects and identifies whether hydrogen, helium and oxygen gases are present in a sample.

Sensors, consisting of light detectors with filters in front of them, are linked to a processing system that can provide a recognisable output to identify each gas.

The filters allow a limited band of wavelengths to pass through them.

The line spectrum for each gas and the position of filters A, B, C and D are shown below.

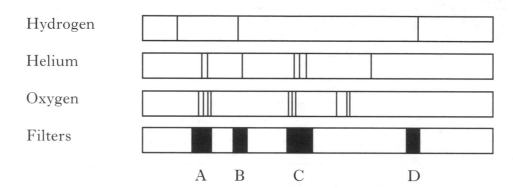

Hydrogen

Helium

Oxygen

Filters

A　　B　　C　　　　D

If a spectral line is at the same position as a filter band then that sensor will produce a logic level one.

(a) Suggest a suitable input device for the sensor.

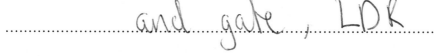

.... and gate , LDR .... ①　1

(b) Complete the truth table for the sensor outputs when each gas is detected. Hydrogen has already been completed.

Gas	Sensor			
	A	B	C	D
Hydrogen	0	1	0	1
Helium				
Oxygen				

2

Marks

9. (continued)

(c) The logic circuit used to identify one of these gases is shown.

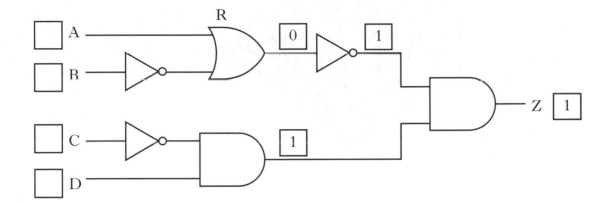

(i) Name logic gate R.

.............OR...........gate.. ⟨1⟩

(ii) When this gas is present, a logic 1 is output at Z.

(A) Complete the boxes A, B, C and D in the logic circuit.

(B) Name which gas is detected with this circuit.

.... 2

[Turn over

Marks

10. A parachutist jumps out of an aircraft. Sometime later, the parachute is opened.

The graph shows the motion of the parachutist from leaving the aircraft until landing.

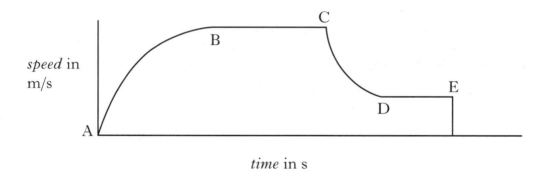

time in s

(a) Which parts of the graph show when the forces acting on the parachutist are balanced?

.... B and D **1**

B + C

D + E

Marks

10. **(continued)**

(*b*) The parachutist lands badly and is airlifted to hospital by helicopter.

cable

The stretcher and parachutist have a total mass of 90·0 kg.

(i) Calculate the weight of the stretcher and parachutist.

> *Space for working and answer*
>
> W = m g
> w = 90 × 10
> W = 900 N

②

(ii) The helicopter cable provides an upward force of 958·5 N to lift the stretcher and parachutist.

Calculate the acceleration of the stretcher and parachutist.

> *Space for working and answer*
>
> A = $\frac{v - u}{t}$
>
> F = m a
> 958·5 N = 90 × a
> = a
> a = 1·065 m/se²

3

Marks

11. Two students set up a linear air track experiment. A linear air track consists of a hollow tube with small holes. Air is blown through the small holes. A vehicle moves on the cushion of air.

The vehicle starts from rest at **X** and moves along the air track so that the card passes through the light gate at point **Y**.

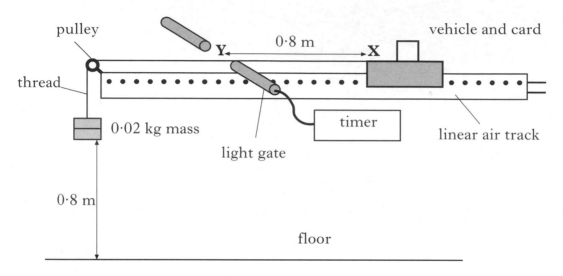

The results for one experiment are recorded in the table below.

Card Length (cm)	Speed at **X** (m/s)	Timer Reading at **Y** (s)	Speed at **Y** (m/s)	Time to travel from **X** to **Y** (s)	Acceleration between **X** and **Y** (m/s²)
3	0	0·05	0·6	1·5	

(a) Use the information given in the table to calculate the acceleration of the vehicle between **X** and **Y**.

Space for working and answer

$\dfrac{v - u}{T}$ $\dfrac{0.6}{1.5}$

$= 0.4 \ m/s^2$

2

Marks

11. (continued)

(b) When repeating the experiment, the 0·02 kg mass detaches from the thread before the vehicle is released. The mass falls 0·80 m to the floor.

(i) Calculate the gravitational potential energy stored in the mass before it fell.

Space for working and answer

$P = Mgh$

$P = 0.02 \times 10 \times 0.8$

$P = 16 \; J$

②

(ii) Assuming the mass falls from rest, calculate the final speed of the mass just before it hits the floor.

Space for working and answer

$Ek = \frac{1}{2} MU^2$

$Ek = 0.02 \times \cancel{} 0.5 \times U^2$

$U^2 = \; 4 \, m/s$

③

[Turn over

K&U | PS

12. A hovercraft service was trialled on the Firth of Forth from Kirkcaldy to Leith.

Marks

The hovercraft and passengers have a total weight of 220 000 N.

(*a*) State the value of the upward force exerted on the hovercraft when it hovers at a constant height.

.... **1**

(*b*) The graph shows how the speed of the hovercraft varies with time for one journey from Kirkcaldy to Leith.

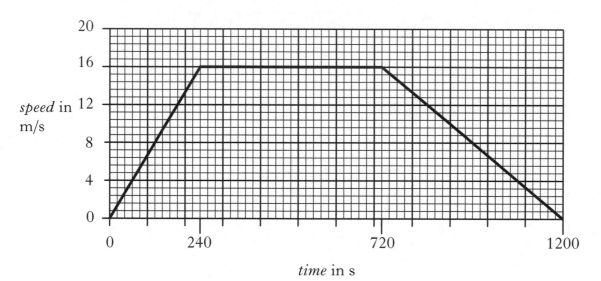

time in s

(i) Calculate the total distance travelled during the journey.

> *Space for working and answer*
>
> $d = s \times t$
>
> $d = 16 \times 1200$
>
> $d =$

2

DO NOT
WRITE IN
THIS
MARGIN

K&U PS

Marks

12. **(b)** **(continued)**

(ii) Calculate the average speed for the whole journey.

> Space for working and answer
>
> $S = d/t$
> $S = 13440 / 1200$
> $S = 11.2$

2

[Turn over

Page twenty-three

Marks

13. The National Grid transfers electrical energy across the country from power stations using a 132 kV network. Electrical power is generated at 20 kV and 5 kA from the power station generator, before being increased to 132 kV using a transformer.

(*a*) What is the reason for increasing the voltage of the electrical power?

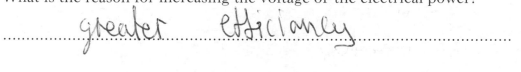

.... greater   efficiency ....

1

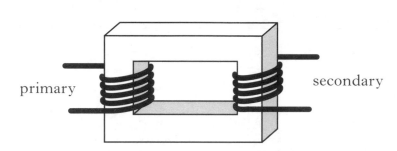

primary   secondary

(*b*) There are 2000 turns in the primary circuit of the transformer. Assuming the transformer is 100% efficient:

(i)   calculate the number of turns in the secondary coil;

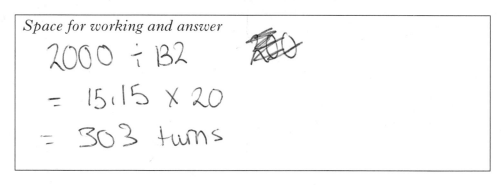

Space for working and answer

2000 ÷ 132

= 15.15 × 20

= 303 turns

2

(ii) calculate the current in the secondary coil of the transformer.

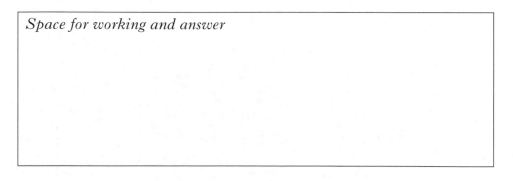

Space for working and answer

2

DO NOT WRITE IN THIS MARGIN

K&U | PS

Marks

13. (continued)

(*c*) The secondary coil of the transformer is connected to the high voltage National Grid network. High voltage cable has a resistance of 0·31 Ω/km. One cable has a length of 220 km.

Calculate the power loss in this cable.

Space for working and answer

3

[Turn over

Marks

14. A solar furnace consists of an array of mirrors which reflect heat radiation on to a central curved reflector.

A heating container is placed at the focus of the central curved reflector. Metals placed in the container are heated until they melt.

The diagram below shows the heat rays after reflection by the mirrors on the hillside.

(*a*) Complete the diagram to show the effect of the central curved reflector on the heat rays.

2

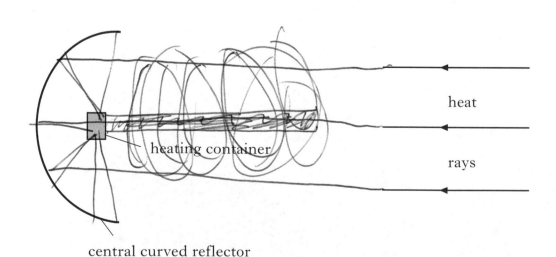

central curved reflector

DO NOT
WRITE IN
THIS
MARGIN

K&U | PS

Marks

14. (continued)

(b) 8000 kg of pre-heated aluminium pellets at a temperature of 160 °C are placed in the container. Aluminium has a specific heat capacity of 902 J/kg °C and a melting point of 660 °C.

How much heat energy is required to heat the aluminium to its melting point?

> Space for working and answer
>
> 902 | ~~500~~ ~~500~~ 500 = ~~5.6~~
> x ~~500~~ 160
> = 288.64

2

(c) (i) How much extra energy is required to melt the aluminium pellets?

> Space for working and answer
>
> 288.64 kJ

3

(ii) The power of the furnace is 800 kW. How long will it take for this extra energy to be supplied?

> Space for working and answer

2

(iii) Explain why it takes longer, in practice, to melt the aluminium.

....

....

1

Page twenty-seven

K&U	PS

Marks

15. A space probe is designed to record data on its way to landing on Ganymede, a moon of Jupiter. The launch vehicle is made up of the probe of mass 8000 kg and the constant thrust rocket unit which has a mass of 117 000 kg.

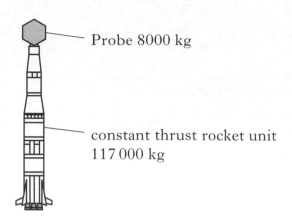

— Probe 8000 kg

— constant thrust rocket unit
117 000 kg

On launch, the resultant force acting upwards on the launch vehicle is 1 400 000 N.

(*a*) Calculate the initial acceleration of the launch vehicle.

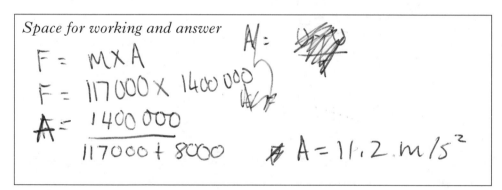

Space for working and answer

$F = M \times A$

$F = 117\,000 \times 1\,400\,000$

$A = \dfrac{1\,400\,000}{117\,000 + 8000}$

$A = 11.2 \, m/s^2$

2

(*b*) As the launch vehicle continues to ascend, its acceleration increases. This is partly due to the decrease in gravitational field strength as it gets further from Earth.

Give another reason why the acceleration increases.

decrease in weight

1

DO NOT
WRITE IN
THIS
MARGIN

K&U | PS

Marks

15. (continued)

(c) The space probe eventually goes into orbit around Ganymede.

probe

Ganymede   Not to scale

Explain why the probe follows a circular path while in orbit.

By the gravitational field

2

(d) The probe has gas thrusters that fire to slow it down in order to land on Ganymede. In terms of Newton's laws, explain how these thrusters achieve this task.

Law 3 Every action has an equal and opposite reaction

2

[Turn over

Marks K&U PS

16. (*a*) Astronomers use refracting telescopes to observe planets. A refracting telescope has an eyepiece lens and an objective lens.

(i) An eyepiece lens can be used on its own as a magnifying glass. Complete the ray diagram to show how the eyepiece lens forms a magnified image.

2

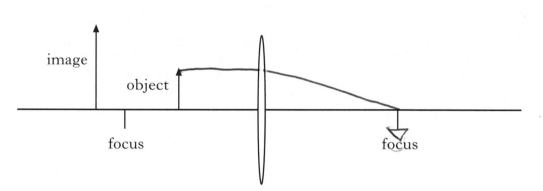

(ii) How does the diameter of the objective lens affect the image seen through the telescope?

..........it affects the size...................

1

DO NOT
WRITE IN
THIS
MARGIN

K&U | PS

Marks

16. (continued)

(b) Radio waves emitted by galaxies are detected and used to provide images of the galaxies.

(i) How does the wavelength of radio waves compare with the wavelength of light?

it's on Par

1

(ii) Name a detector for radio waves.

a Radio

1

(iii) Why are different kinds of telescope used to detect signals from space?

different sizes
of signal

1

[END OF QUESTION PAPER]

52/100

ADDITIONAL SPACE FOR ANSWERS

Make sure you write the correct question number beside each answer.

STANDARD GRADE | CREDIT

2010

[BLANK PAGE]

FOR OFFICIAL USE

K&U   PS

C

3220/402

NATIONAL
QUALIFICATIONS
2010

FRIDAY, 28 MAY
10.50 AM – 12.35 PM

PHYSICS
STANDARD GRADE
Credit Level

Fill in these boxes and read what is printed below.

Full name of centre

Town

Forename(s)

Surname

Date of birth

Day	Month	Year

Scottish candidate number

Number of seat

Reference may be made to the Physics Data Booklet.

1 All questions should be answered.

2 The questions may be answered in any order but all answers must be written clearly and legibly in this book.

3 Write your answer where indicated by the question or in the space provided after the question.

4 If you change your mind about your answer you may score it out and rewrite it in the space provided at the end of the answer book.

5 If you use the additional space at the end of the answer book for answering any questions, you **must** write the correct question number beside each answer.

6 Before leaving the examination room you must give this book to the Invigilator. If you do not, you may lose all the marks for this paper.

7 Any necessary data will be found in the **data sheet** on page three.

8 Care should be taken to give an appropriate number of significant figures in the final answers to questions.

Use **blue** or **black ink**. Pencil may be used for graphs and diagrams only.

[BLANK PAGE]

DATA SHEET

Speed of light in materials

Material	Speed in m/s
Air	3.0×10^8
Carbon dioxide	3.0×10^8
Diamond	1.2×10^8
Glass	2.0×10^8
Glycerol	2.1×10^8
Water	2.3×10^8

Speed of sound in materials

Material	Speed in m/s
Aluminium	5200
Air	340
Bone	4100
Carbon dioxide	270
Glycerol	1900
Muscle	1600
Steel	5200
Tissue	1500
Water	1500

Gravitational field strengths

	Gravitational field strength on the surface in N/kg
Earth	10
Jupiter	26
Mars	4
Mercury	4
Moon	1.6
Neptune	12
Saturn	11
Sun	270
Venus	9

Specific heat capacity of materials

Material	Specific heat capacity in J/kg °C
Alcohol	2350
Aluminium	902
Copper	386
Glass	500
Glycerol	2400
Ice	2100
Lead	128
Silica	1033
Water	4180

Specific latent heat of fusion of materials

Material	Specific latent heat of fusion in J/kg
Alcohol	0.99×10^5
Aluminium	3.95×10^5
Carbon dioxide	1.80×10^5
Copper	2.05×10^5
Glycerol	1.81×10^5
Lead	0.25×10^5
Water	3.34×10^5

Melting and boiling points of materials

Material	Melting point in °C	Boiling point in °C
Alcohol	−98	65
Aluminium	660	2470
Copper	1077	2567
Glycerol	18	290
Lead	328	1737
Turpentine	−10	156

Specific latent heat of vaporisation of materials

Material	Specific latent heat of vaporisation in J/kg
Alcohol	11.2×10^5
Carbon dioxide	3.77×10^5
Glycerol	8.30×10^5
Turpentine	2.90×10^5
Water	22.6×10^5

SI Prefixes and Multiplication Factors

Prefix	Symbol	Factor	
giga	G	1 000 000 000	$= 10^9$
mega	M	1 000 000	$= 10^6$
kilo	k	1000	$= 10^3$
milli	m	0.001	$= 10^{-3}$
micro	μ	0.000 001	$= 10^{-6}$
nano	n	0.000 000 001	$= 10^{-9}$

Marks

1. A car is fitted with a parking system. This warns the driver how close objects are behind the car. Equipment on the rear bumper of the car transmits ultrasound waves and receives the reflected waves.

(a) (i) Use the data sheet to find the speed of ultrasound waves in air.

....   **1**

(ii) The ultrasound waves have a frequency of 40 kHz.

Calculate the wavelength of these waves.

Space for working and answer

2

(b) The car stops 1·7 m from a wall.

Calculate the time for a transmitted wave to return to the car.

Space for working and answer

3

(c) The car is moved closer to the wall.

State what happens to the time for a transmitted wave to return to the car.

....

....   **1**

Marks

2. A hill lies between a radio and television transmitter and a house.

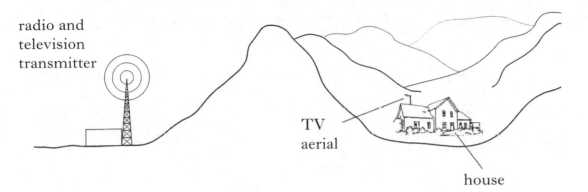

radio and television transmitter

TV aerial

house

The house is within the range of both the radio and television signals from the transmitter.

(*a*) In the house, a radio has good reception but a TV has poor reception from this transmitter.

Suggest an explanation for this.

....

....

....

.... **2**

(*b*) The house is also fitted with a dish aerial to receive TV signals from a geostationary satellite. The TV signals are carried by microwaves with a frequency of 12 GHz.

   (i) State the speed of microwave signals in air.

.... **1**

   (ii) What is meant by the term geostationary?

....

.... **1**

[Turn over

Marks

3. The circuit shown is used to control the brightness of two **identical** lamps. The variable resistor is adjusted until the lamps operate at their correct voltage of 3·0 V.

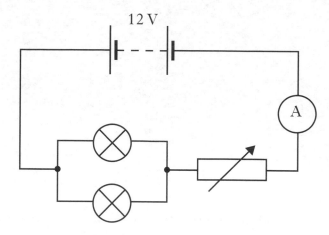

12 V

A

(*a*) When the lamps operate at the correct voltage, the reading on the ammeter is 1·2 A.

Calculate the current in one lamp.

Space for working and answer

1

(*b*) Calculate the resistance of one lamp.

Space for working and answer

2

Marks

3. **(continued)**

(c) Calculate the combined resistance of the two lamps in this circuit.

> *Space for working and answer*

2

(d) When the lamps operate at their correct voltage the resistance of the variable resistor is $7 \cdot 5\,\Omega$.

Calculate the total resistance in the circuit.

> *Space for working and answer*

2

(e) One of the lamps is removed.

   (i) What happens to the reading on the ammeter?

   1

   (ii) Justify your answer.

   1

[Turn over

Marks

4. A washing machine contains a commercial electric motor. The rating plate on the washing machine shows the following information.

> **2530 W**
>
> **230 V ac**
>
> **50 Hz**

The plug connected to the washing machine contains a 13 A fuse.

(a) (i) State the purpose of the fuse.

.... **1**

(ii) Show by calculation that a 3 A fuse is unsuitable.

Space for working and answer

2

Marks

4. (continued)

(b) A student builds a simple dc electric motor. Some differences between a commercial motor and a simple dc motor are shown in the table.

Commercial motor	Simple dc motor
field coils	permanent magnets
multi-section commutator	commutator
carbon brushes	brushes

State a reason for a commercial motor using:

(i) field coils instead of permanent magnets;

.... **1**

(ii) a multi-section commutator instead of a single commutator.

.... **1**

(c) The electrical energy used by a commercial motor is measured in kilowatt-hours.

Calculate how many joules are equivalent to one kilowatt-hour.

Space for working and answer

2

[Turn over

Marks

5. In the eye, refraction of light occurs at both the cornea and the lens.

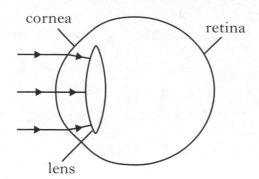

(*a*) The focal length of an eye lens system (the cornea and the lens together) is 22 mm.

Calculate the power of this eye lens system.

Space for working and answer

2

Marks

5. (continued)

(b) A student has an eye defect. An object close to the student's eye appears focused but a distant object appears blurred.

    (i) What name is given to this eye defect?

    1

    (ii) The diagram shows rays of light, from a distant object, entering the student's eye.

    Complete the diagram to show how the light rays reach the retina of the student's eye. 1

    (iii) By referring to your completed diagram, explain why the image on the retina of the student's eye is blurred.

    1

    (iv) A lens is used to correct this eye defect.

    Draw the shape of this lens.

Space for drawing

1

Marks

6. The table gives information about radioactive substances used in medicine.

Radioactive substance	Type of ionising radiation emitted	Half-life
iodine-131	beta and gamma	8 days
technetium-99 m	gamma	6 hours
cobalt-60	beta and gamma	5·3 years

(a) (i) State what is meant by the term ionisation.

....

....   **1**

(ii) State a type of ionising radiation **not** given in the table above.

....   **1**

(b) A sample of iodine-131 is delivered to a hospital 24 days before it is given to a patient. The activity of the iodine-131 when it is given to the patient is 6 MBq.

Calculate the initial activity, in MBq, of the sample when it was delivered to the hospital.

Space for working and answer

2

Marks

6. (continued)

(c) (i) Equivalent dose measures the biological effect of radiation.

State the unit of equivalent dose.

.... **1**

(ii) For living material the biological effect of radiation depends on a number of factors.

State **two** of these factors.

1 ....

2 .... **2**

[Turn over

7. A physics student builds a lap counter for a toy racing car set. The lap is counted when the car passes over the light sensor.

light sensor

(*a*) The circuit for the light sensor contains an LDR as shown.

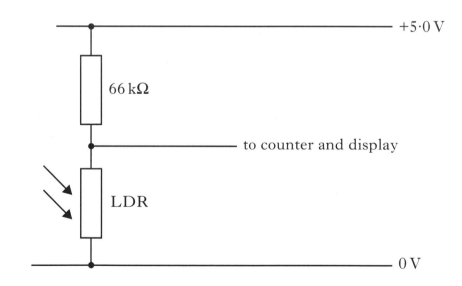

+5·0 V

66 kΩ

to counter and display

LDR

0 V

The resistance of the LDR for different conditions is shown in the table.

Light Sensor	Resistance of LDR (kΩ)
covered	22
uncovered	2

Marks

7. **(a)** **(continued)**

Calculate the voltage across the LDR when the light sensor is covered.

> *Space for working and answer*

3

(b) (i) The system contains a counter and display. The output of the counter is **binary**. This is then converted to **decimal** and shown on the display. What decimal number is shown when the counter output is 1001?

.... 1

(ii) The system also contains a buzzer. The buzzer emits a sound when a car completes a lap. The buzzer has a resistance of $120\,\Omega$ and a power of 147 mW.

Calculate the voltage across the buzzer when it sounds.

> *Space for working and answer*

2

[Turn over

K&U	PS

Marks

8. An electronic device warns a car driver when the seat belt has not been fastened. The device only operates when the ignition is switched on. The device contains the logic circuit shown.

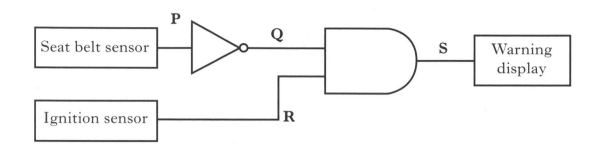

The seat belt sensor produces logic 1 when the seat belt is fastened and logic 0 when the seat belt is unfastened.

The ignition sensor produces logic 1 when the car ignition is on and logic 0 when the car ignition is off.

(a) (i) Suggest a suitable output device that will illuminate the warning display.

....   1

(ii) Complete the truth table for the logic levels **P**, **Q** and **S** in the circuit.

Seat belt	Ignition	**P**	**Q**	**R**	**S**
unfastened	off			0	
unfastened	on			1	
fastened	off			0	
fastened	on			1	

3

(b) Explain in terms of forces, why seat belts are used in cars.

....

....

....   2

DO NOT WRITE IN THIS MARGIN

K&U PS

Marks

8. (continued)

(*c*) The car has another electronic device that also contains a logic gate. The truth table for **this** logic gate is shown below.

Input 1	Input 2	Output
0	0	0
0	1	1
1	0	1
1	1	1

(i) Name this logic gate.

.... **1**

(ii) Draw the symbol for this logic gate.

Space for symbol

1

(*d*) The temperature outside the car is measured with an electronic thermometer and displayed on a screen.

What input device could be used in the electronic thermometer?

.... **1**

[Turn over

Marks

9. A student releases a trolley from rest near the top of a track. The trolley moves down the track. A card attached to the trolley passes through a light gate near the bottom of the track.

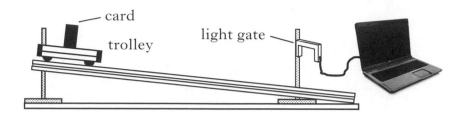

(a) The student records the following information.

Length of the card = 60 mm
Distance travelled by the trolley down the track = 1·2 m
Time for the card to pass through the light gate = 0·075 s

Calculate the instantaneous speed of the trolley as it passes through the light gate.

> *Space for working and answer*

2

(b) The mass of the trolley is 0·55 kg.

Calculate its kinetic energy as it passes through the light gate.

> *Space for working and answer*

2

(c) Suggest a possible value for the average speed of the trolley over the 1·2 m distance travelled by the trolley down the track.

.... **1**

Marks

10. A cyclist is approaching traffic lights at a constant speed. The cyclist sees the lights change to red. The graph shows how the speed of the cyclist varies with time from the instant the cyclist sees the lights change to red.

(*a*) (i) How long did it take for the cyclist to react before applying the brakes?

....   **1**

(ii) Calculate the distance travelled from the instant the cyclist sees the traffic lights change to red until stationary.

Space for working and answer

2

(*b*) The cyclist now sees the traffic lights change to green and accelerates away from the lights. The combined mass of the cycle and cyclist is 75 kg. An unbalanced force of 150 N acts on this combined mass.

Calculate the acceleration.

Space for working and answer

2

Marks

11. A wind generator is used to charge a 12 V battery. The charging current depends on the wind speed.

The graph shows the charging current at different wind speeds.

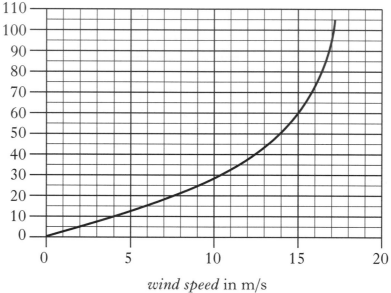

charging current in A

wind speed in m/s

(*a*) During one charge of the battery, the wind speed is constant at 15 m/s. During this time a charge of 4500 C is transferred to the battery.

Calculate the time taken to transfer this charge to the battery.

Space for working and answer

3

Marks

11. (continued)

(b) At another wind speed the generator has an output power of 120 W and is 30% efficient.

Calculate the input power to the generator.

> *Space for working and answer*

2

(c) A bicycle has a small generator called a dynamo. The dynamo contains a magnet which spins near a coil of wire.

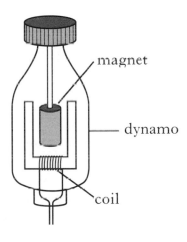

When the magnet spins, a voltage is induced in the coil.

State **two** factors that affect the size of the induced voltage.

1 ....

2   2

[Turn over

K&U   PS

Marks

12. A technician tests an electric kettle. The kettle is filled with water and switched on for 3 minutes.

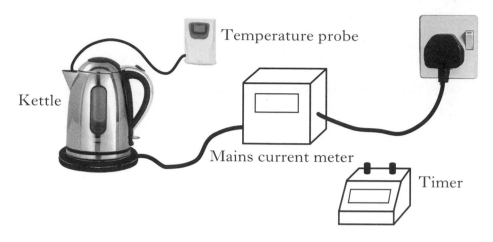

The technician records the following information.

Current = 12·5 A	
Voltage = 230 V	
Time = 3 minutes	
Initial temperature = 18 °C	
Final temperature = 90 °C	

(*a*) (i) Show that 517 500 J of electrical energy is supplied to the kettle in 3 minutes.

Space for working and answer

2

Marks

12. (*a*) (**continued**)

(ii) Calculate the mass of water in the kettle.

> *Space for working and answer*

3

(iii) Explain why the mass of water will be less than calculated in (*a*)(ii).

.... **1**

(*b*) The technician tests a second kettle. When the water boils this kettle does not switch off and continues to heat the water.

(i) State what happens to the temperature of the water when it boils.

.... **1**

While the water is boiling, the kettle supplies 565 000 J of heat energy to the water.

(ii) Calculate the mass of water changed into steam.

> *Space for working and answer*

3

[Turn over

Marks

13. During a visit to a science centre a student learns more about gravitational field strength.

(a) State what is meant by gravitational field strength.

....

.... 1

(b) The science centre has a set of specially designed scales. The weight of the student on different planets in the solar system can be found by using these scales. The student stands on each of these scales in turn. The weight on each of these scales is shown.

Mercury
280 N

Planet X
630 N

Neptune
840 N

(i) The student has a mass of 70 kg.

Calculate the gravitational field strength on Planet X.

Space for working and answer

2

(ii) Identify Planet X.

.... 1

13. (continued)

(c) The student watches a short film. This film shows an astronaut dropping a hammer onto the surface of the Moon. The hammer takes 1·2 s to fall to the Moon's surface. The gravitational field strength on the Moon is 1·6 N/kg.

(i) Calculate the vertical speed of the hammer just before it strikes the Moon's surface.

> *Space for working and answer*

2

(ii) The film then shows the astronaut throwing the hammer horizontally from the same height.

How long does it take for the hammer to fall to the Moon's surface?

.... **1**

[Turn over

Marks

14. The diagram represents the electromagnetic spectrum.

Some of the radiations have not been named.

gamma	X-rays	P	Visible light	Q	microwaves	Radio and TV

Electromagnetic spectrum

increasing frequency

(a) (i) Name radiations P and Q.

P ....

Q **2**

(ii) Which radiation in the electromagnetic spectrum has the shortest wavelength?

.... **1**

(iii) State **one** detector of radio waves.

.... **1**

(iv) State **one** medical use of infrared radiation.

.... **1**

(b) Yellow light is part of the visible spectrum. The wavelength of yellow light is $5 \cdot 9 \times 10^{-7}$ m.

The visible spectrum also contains red, blue and green light.

Use the information above to complete the following table.

Colour	Wavelength (m)
	7×10^{-7}
yellow	
	$5 \cdot 5 \times 10^{-7}$
	$4 \cdot 5 \times 10^{-7}$

2

Marks

14. (continued)

(c) The table below gives information about planets that orbit the Sun.

Planet	Distance from the Sun (Gm)	Period (days)	Mass (Earth masses)
Earth	150	365	1
Jupiter	780		318
Mars	228	687	0·11
Mercury	58	88	0·06
Saturn	1430	10 760	95
Venus	110	225	0·82

(i) Give an approximate value, **in days**, for the period of Jupiter.

.... **1**

(ii) Calculate the time taken for light from the Sun to reach Saturn.

Space for working and answer

3

[*END OF QUESTION PAPER*]

ADDITIONAL SPACE FOR ANSWERS

Make sure you write the correct question number beside each answer.

STANDARD GRADE | CREDIT

2011

[BLANK PAGE]

FOR OFFICIAL USE

C

K&U   PS

3220/402

NATIONAL
QUALIFICATIONS
2011

MONDAY, 23 MAY
10.50 AM – 12.35 PM

PHYSICS
STANDARD GRADE
Credit Level

Fill in these boxes and read what is printed below.

Full name of centre

Town

Forename(s)

Surname

Date of birth

Day   Month   Year

Scottish candidate number

Number of seat

Reference may be made to the Physics Data Booklet.

1 All questions should be answered.

2 The questions may be answered in any order but all answers must be written clearly and legibly in this book.

3 Write your answer where indicated by the question or in the space provided after the question.

4 If you change your mind about your answer you may score it out and rewrite it in the space provided at the end of the answer book.

5 If you use the additional space at the end of the answer book for answering any questions, you **must** write the correct question number beside each answer.

6 Before leaving the examination room you must give this book to the Invigilator. If you do not, you may lose all the marks for this paper.

7 Any necessary data will be found in the **data sheet** on page three.

8 Care should be taken to give an appropriate number of significant figures in the final answers to questions.

Use **blue** or **black ink**. Pencil may be used for graphs and diagrams only.

[BLANK PAGE]

DATA SHEET

Speed of light in materials

Material	Speed in m/s
Air	3.0×10^8
Carbon dioxide	3.0×10^8
Diamond	1.2×10^8
Glass	2.0×10^8
Glycerol	2.1×10^8
Water	2.3×10^8

Speed of sound in materials

Material	Speed in m/s
Aluminium	5200
Air	340
Bone	4100
Carbon dioxide	270
Glycerol	1900
Muscle	1600
Steel	5200
Tissue	1500
Water	1500

Gravitational field strengths

	Gravitational field strength on the surface in N/kg
Earth	10
Jupiter	26
Mars	4
Mercury	4
Moon	1.6
Neptune	12
Saturn	11
Sun	270
Venus	9

Specific heat capacity of materials

Material	Specific heat capacity in J/kg °C
Alcohol	2350
Aluminium	902
Copper	386
Glass	500
Glycerol	2400
Ice	2100
Lead	128
Silica	1033
Water	4180

Specific latent heat of fusion of materials

Material	Specific latent heat of fusion in J/kg
Alcohol	0.99×10^5
Aluminium	3.95×10^5
Carbon dioxide	1.80×10^5
Copper	2.05×10^5
Glycerol	1.81×10^5
Lead	0.25×10^5
Water	3.34×10^5

Melting and boiling points of materials

Material	Melting point in °C	Boiling point in °C
Alcohol	−98	65
Aluminium	660	2470
Copper	1077	2567
Glycerol	18	290
Lead	328	1737
Turpentine	−10	156

Specific latent heat of vaporisation of materials

Material	Specific latent heat of vaporisation in J/kg
Alcohol	11.2×10^5
Carbon dioxide	3.77×10^5
Glycerol	8.30×10^5
Turpentine	2.90×10^5
Water	22.6×10^5

SI Prefixes and Multiplication Factors

Prefix	Symbol	Factor	
giga	G	1 000 000 000	$= 10^9$
mega	M	1 000 000	$= 10^6$
kilo	k	1000	$= 10^3$
milli	m	0.001	$= 10^{-3}$
micro	μ	0.000 001	$= 10^{-6}$
nano	n	0.000 000 001	$= 10^{-9}$

Marks

1. A mountain climber carries a device which receives radio signals from satellites to determine the climber's position.

The device can also be used to send the climber's position to the emergency services in the event of an accident.

emergency alert button

(a) One satellite sends a radio signal that is received by the device 0·068 s after transmission.

(i) State the speed of the radio signal.

.... 1

(ii) Calculate the distance between this satellite and the climber.

Space for working and answer

2

Marks | K&U | PS

1. **(continued)**

(b) The device sends a radio signal to the emergency services.

The frequency of the signal is 2100 MHz.

Calculate the wavelength of this signal.

Space for working and answer

2

(c) The emergency services use a telephone to contact the nearest mountain rescue team.

A student examines the electrical signal from a telephone mouthpiece. An oscilloscope is connected to the mouthpiece and displays an electrical signal when the student whistles into the mouthpiece.

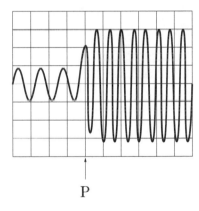

P

State and describe what happens at point P on the signal pattern to:

A   the loudness of the sound;

....

.... 1

B   the frequency of the sound.

....

.... 1

2. A rugby match is being played at Murrayfield. Spectators are able to view close-up images and replays of the match on giant screens.

(a) Each screen is composed of millions of clusters of LEDs. The diagram below shows one of these clusters.

A cluster
of LEDs

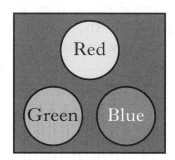

(i) In one cluster all LEDs are switched on.

State the colour observed on the screen in this area.

.... 1

(ii) The green LED in this cluster is now switched off.

What colour is observed?

.... 1

Marks

2.   **(continued)**

(b) The LED screens are controlled by a computer which receives images from pitch-side cameras.

The computer is linked to the screens using optical fibres.

(i) Describe how signals are transmitted along optical fibres.

....

....

....   **2**

(ii) State **one** advantage of using optical fibres rather than copper wires for transmitting the signals.

....

....   **1**

[Turn over

3. A mains electric fire has two heating elements which can be switched on and off separately. The heating elements can be switched on to produce three different heat settings: LOW, MEDIUM and HIGH. The fire also has an interior lamp which can be switched on to give a log-burning effect.

The circuit diagram for the fire is shown.

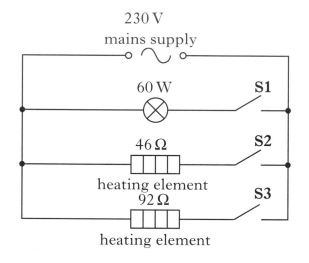

(a) When switch **S1** is closed, the lamp operates at its stated rating of 60 W. Calculate the current in the lamp.

Space for working and answer

2

Marks

3.   (continued)

(b)   Switch **S1** is opened and switches **S2** and **S3** are closed.

   (i)   Calculate the combined resistance of both heating elements.

   Space for working and answer

   2

   (ii)   Calculate the total power developed in the heating elements when **S2** and **S3** are closed.

   Space for working and answer

   2

   (iii)   State and explain which switch or switches would have to be closed to produce the **LOW** heat setting.

   ....

   ....

     2

[Turn over

Marks | K&U | PS

4. The diagram shows three household circuits connected to a consumer unit.

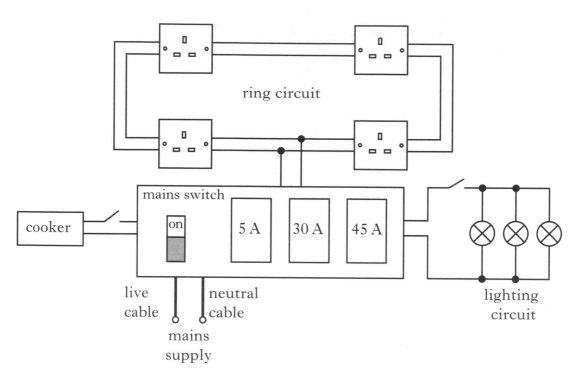

The consumer unit contains a mains switch and three fuses.

The mains supply is also connected to the consumer unit.

The earth wires for these circuits are not shown in the diagram.

(a) Explain why the mains switch must be connected to the live cable from the mains supply.

....

.... 1

(b) (i) Complete the table below to show which value of fuse should be connected to each circuit.

Circuit	Value of fuse
Lighting Circuit	
Cooker	45 A
Ring Circuit	

1

Marks

4. **(b)** **(continued)**

(ii) The lighting circuit and the ring circuit have different values of fuse.

State another difference between the ring circuit and the lighting circuit.

....   **1**

(c) State **one** advantage of using a ring circuit as a preferred method of wiring in parallel.

....

....   **1**

(d) Circuit breakers can be used in a consumer unit instead of fuses.

State **one** advantage of using a circuit breaker instead of a fuse.

....

....   **1**

[Turn over

Marks   K&U   PS

5. A patient visits an ophthalmologist for an eye examination.

The ophthalmologist uses ultrasound to take measurements inside the eye.

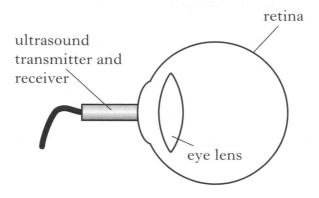

(*a*) What name describes the shape of the eye lens?

....

1

(*b*) The ophthalmologist has a graph obtained using measurements from a person with normal eyesight. The graph shows times to receive reflected ultrasound pulses from the **front** edge of the eye lens, the **back** edge of the eye lens and from the **retina**.

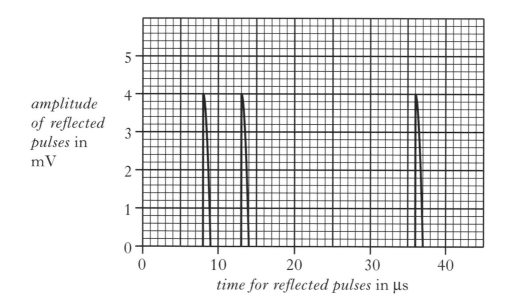

(i) Calculate the time taken for the ultrasound to travel from the **front** edge to the **back** edge of the eye lens.

Space for working and answer

2

Marks

K&U PS

5. **(b)** **(continued)**

(ii) Ultrasound pulses travel at a speed of 1500 m/s inside the lens.

Calculate the thickness of the lens in the normal-sighted person.

Space for working and answer

2

(c) Another set of measurements indicates that a patient is long-sighted and requires spectacles. Figure 1 shows rays of light from a book entering an eye of this patient until the rays reach the retina.

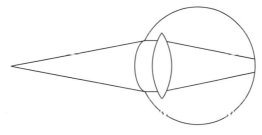

Figure 1

(i) In the dotted box in Figure 2, draw the shape of lens that would correct this eye defect.

1

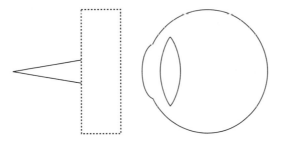

Figure 2

(ii) In Figure 2, complete the path of the rays of light from this lens until they reach the retina.

2

(iii) One lens used has a power of 1·4 D.

Calculate its focal length.

Space for working and answer

2

Marks   K&U | PS

6. A teacher is demonstrating absorption of alpha, beta and gamma radiations.

(a) The teacher explains that when these radiations are absorbed they may cause ionisation in the absorbing material.

(i) Which of the two diagrams below represents an ionised atom?

Explain your answer.

○ proton
◉ neutron
• electron

diagram 1   *diagram 2*

....

....   **2**

(ii) Which type of radiation: alpha, beta or gamma causes most ionisation?

....   **1**

(b) The radioactive sources are stored in lead-lined boxes. This is a safety precaution to minimise exposure of students and teacher to radiations from the sources.

State **one** further safety precaution that should be taken by the teacher when handling the radioactive sources.

....   **1**

(c) Radioactive materials are used in hospitals.

(i) Describe **one** medical use of radiation where the radiation is used to destroy cells.

....   **1**

Marks

K&U   PS

6. (c) (continued)

(ii) A hospital physicist is working with some radioactive materials. The physicist wears a badge containing photographic film. Light cannot reach the film.

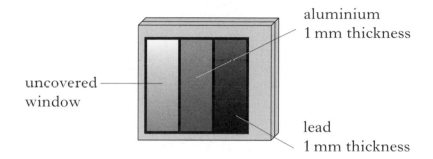

uncovered window

aluminium 1 mm thickness

lead 1 mm thickness

When developed, it is found that the film behind both the uncovered window and the window covered with 1 mm thick aluminium have turned black.

State which type of radiation could cause the film in **only** these areas to turn black.

....   1

(iii) It is found that the physicist has received an equivalent dose of 2 mSv due to this radiation.

(A) In the sentence below, circle **one** phrase in the brackets to make the statement correct.

The effect of an equivalent dose of 2 mSv of gamma radiation

is $\left\{ \begin{array}{l} \text{the same as} \\ \text{greater than} \\ \text{less than} \end{array} \right\}$ an equivalent dose of 2 mSv of beta

radiation.   1

(B) Explain your answer.

....

....   1

[Turn over

Marks | K&U | PS

7. An automatic hand dryer used in a washroom is shown in the diagram below.

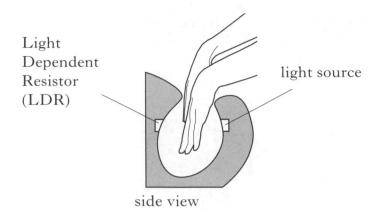

Light
Dependent
Resistor
(LDR)

light source

side view

Inserting hands into the dryer breaks a light beam, this is detected using a light dependent resistor (LDR). The LDR is part of a switching circuit which activates the dryer when hands are inserted.

Part of the circuit for the hand dryer is shown.

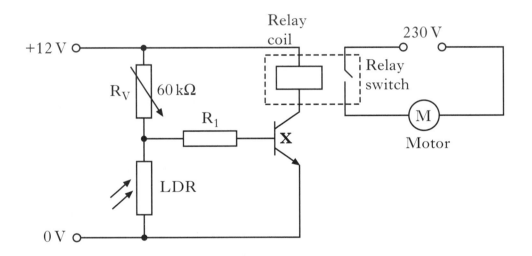

(a) The variable resistor R_V is set to a resistance of $60\,k\Omega$.

Calculate the voltage across the LDR when its resistance is $4\,k\Omega$.

Space for working and answer

2

Marks

7. (continued)

(b) Name component **X** in the circuit diagram.

....   **1**

(c) Explain how this circuit operates to activate the motor in the dryer when the light level falls below a certain value.

....

....

....

....

....   **2**

[Turn over

Marks | K&U | PS

8. A house is fitted with a burglar alarm. The outside doors are fitted with magnetic contact switches that detect a door being opened. An infra-red sensor detects movement inside the house. An alarm box produces flashes of light and pulses of sound when activated.

The alarm system can be switched on or off using a master switch.

— Alarm box

The logic circuit for part of the alarm system is shown below.

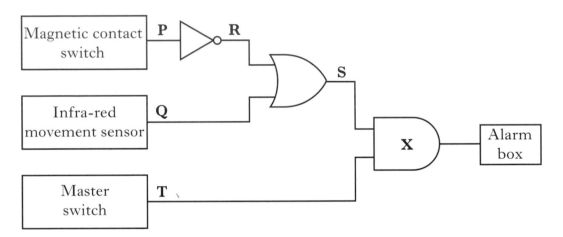

When a door is opened, the logic level at **P** changes from logic **1** to logic **0**.

When the infra-red movement sensor detects movement, the logic level at **Q** changes from logic **0** to logic **1**.

When the master switch is **ON**, the logic level at **T** is logic **1**.

(a) Complete the truth table below to show the logic levels at **R** and **S** in the logic circuit.

P	Q	R	S
0	0		
1	0		
0	1		
1	1		

2

8. (continued)

(*b*) (i) Name the logic gate **X** shown in the logic circuit.

.... 1

(ii) Explain why this type of gate must be connected to the master switch to allow the alarm box to be switched OFF.

....

.... 1

(iii) Name a suitable output device that could be used in the alarm box to produce an audio output.

.... 1

[Turn over

Marks

K&U PS

9. On a visit to a theme park, four students ride the log flume.

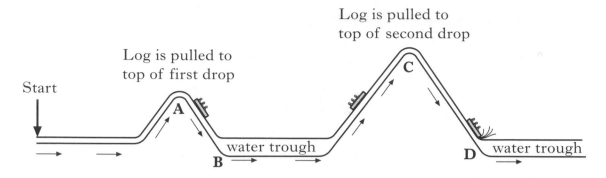

Log is pulled to
top of second drop

Log is pulled to
top of first drop

Start

water trough   water trough

Not to scale

(a) The graph shows how the speed of the log varies during the ride.

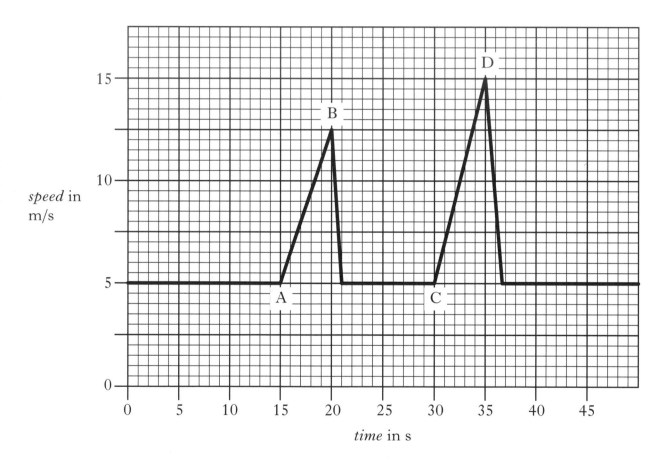

speed in m/s

time in s

(i) Describe the motion of the log during **AB** on the graph.

....   1

9. (a) (continued)

    (ii) Calculate the distance travelled by the log from the start of the ride to the bottom of the first drop.

        Space for working and answer

        2

    (iii) Calculate the log's acceleration as it goes down the second drop.

        Space for working and answer

        2

  (b) Describe how the instantaneous speed of the log could be measured at position **D** on the log flume.

    ....

    ....

    ....

    ....

    3

[Turn over

Marks

10. Two students are playing a game of air hockey. An air hockey table has small holes in its surface through which air is blown. A **mallet** is used to strike the **puck**. The puck moves off on the cushion of air.

puck

mallet

(*a*) The puck has a mass of 35 g.

Calculate the weight of the puck.

Space for working and answer

2

(*b*) The puck is struck by the mallet and moves off with a speed of 4·0 m/s.

(i) State the speed at which the puck hits the side cushion.

.... 1

(ii) Explain your answer.

....

.... 1

10. (continued)

(c) The air supply to the table is switched off. This time the puck leaves the mallet with a speed of 8·0 m/s. A frictional force between the puck and the table causes the puck to stop moving after it has travelled a certain distance.

(i) Calculate the kinetic energy of the puck as it leaves the mallet.

Space for working and answer

2

(ii) The average frictional force acting on the puck is 5·0 N.

Calculate the distance travelled by the puck.

Space for working and answer

3

[Turn over

Marks K&U PS

11. A steam cleaner rated at 2 kW is used to clean a carpet. The water tank is filled with 1·6 kg of water at 20 °C. This water is heated until it boils and produces steam. The brush head is pushed across the surface of the carpet and steam is released.

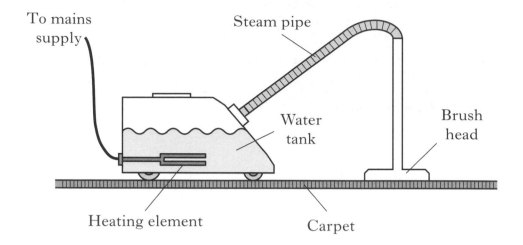

(a) Calculate how much heat energy is needed to bring this water to its boiling point of 100 °C.

Space for working and answer

3

(b) After the steam cleaner has been used for a period of time, 0·9 kg of boiling water has changed into steam.

(i) Calculate how much heat energy was needed to do this.

Space for working and answer

3

DO NOT WRITE IN THIS MARGIN

Marks	K&U	PS

11. (*b*) (continued)

(ii) Calculate how long it would take to change this water into steam.

Space for working and answer

2

[Turn over

Marks | K&U | PS

12. A small submersible pump is used in a garden water fountain. The pump raises 25 kg of water each minute from a reservoir at ground level.

The water travels through a plastic tube and reaches a height of 1·2 m above ground level.

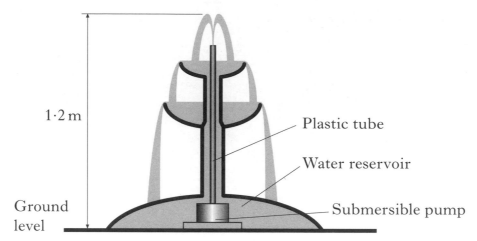

(a) Calculate how much gravitational potential energy the water gains each minute.

> *Space for working and answer*

2

(b) (i) The pump system is 40% efficient.

Calculate the input power in watts.

> *Space for working and answer*

3

(ii) Give **two** reasons why the pump system is not 100% efficient.

....

.... 2

Marks

K&U | PS

13. A car driver exits a car park having accidentally left a package resting on the roof of the car. The car is travelling at a constant speed of 15 m/s when the driver brakes suddenly and the car stops. The package continues to move forward.

package

(a) (i) On the above diagram sketch the path taken by the package.

1

(ii) Explain why the package follows this path.

....

....

....

2

(b) The package takes 0·55 s to fall to the ground.

Calculate its vertical speed as it reaches the ground.

Space for working and answer

3

[Turn over

Marks

14. All stars emit electromagnetic radiation. The diagram below shows the electromagnetic spectrum in order of increasing wavelength. The names of **three** of the radiations are missing.

Gamma rays	X-rays	P	Visible light	Q	R	TV and Radio

Increasing wavelength

(*a*) (i) Name radiation:

P ....

Q ....

R **2**

(ii) Which radiation in the electromagnetic spectrum has the lowest frequency?

.... **1**

14. (continued)

(b) Some spectral lines of radiation from a distant star are shown below.

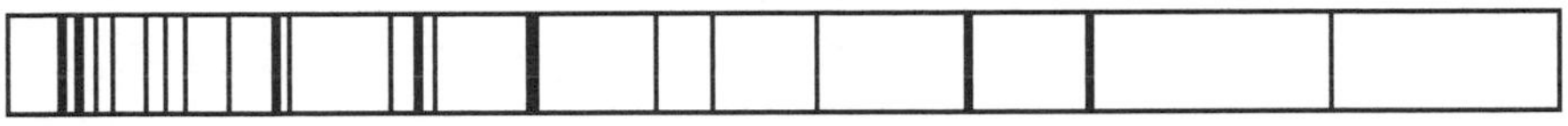

Spectral lines of radiation from distant star

The spectral lines of a number of elements are also shown.

Cadmium

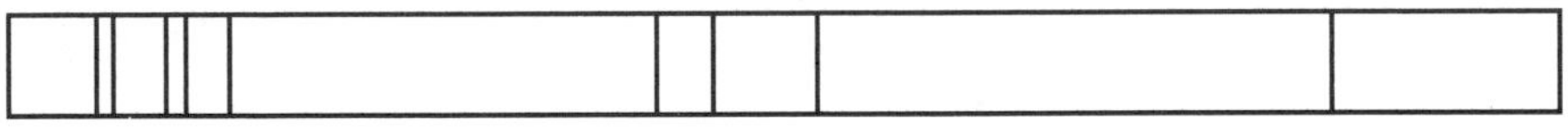

Calcium

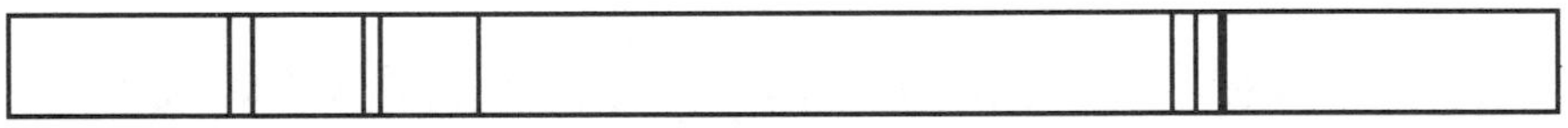

Krypton

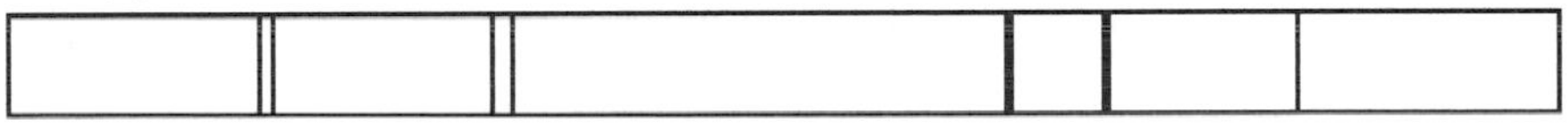

Mercury

Use the spectral lines of the elements shown above to identify which of these elements are present in the distant star.

....   2

[Turn over for Question 15 on *Page thirty*

Marks

DO NOT
WRITE IN
THIS
MARGIN

K&U PS

15. The first manned space flights took place 50 years ago. Spacecraft were launched into space using powerful rockets.

(a) The operation of a rocket engine can be explained using Newton's Third Law of Motion.

   (i) State Newton's Third Law of Motion.

   ....

   .... **1**

   (ii) Explain, in terms of Newton's Third Law, how the rocket engines propel the rocket upwards.

   ....

   .... **1**

(b) At lift-off, one rocket has a total mass of $2 \cdot 05 \times 10^6$ kg. The resultant force acting upwards on the rocket is $8 \cdot 2 \times 10^6$ N.

Calculate the acceleration of the rocket at lift-off.

Space for working and answer

2

[END OF QUESTION PAPER]

ADDITIONAL SPACE FOR ANSWERS

Make sure you write the correct question number beside each answer.

ADDITIONAL SPACE FOR ANSWERS

Make sure you write the correct question number beside each answer.

STANDARD GRADE | ANSWER SECTION

SQA STANDARD GRADE CREDIT PHYSICS
2007–2011

1. (a) 3×10^8 m/s

   (b) $\lambda = 0.16$ m

   (c) t = 0.24 s

2. (a) medium freqency

   (b) (i) surface waves
   (ii) longer wavelength
   (iii) the radio waves are reflected by the ionosphere.
   (iv) Answer needs to mention satellite and any valid function such as:
   - signals transmitted back to Earth
   - signal amplified/focused
   - signal frequency altered.

3. (a) (i)

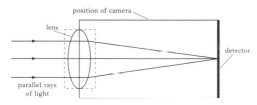

   (ii) P = 62.5 D

   (b) • Line build up is when electrons scan across screen.
   • Image retention is when brain/eye retains each picture while next is produced (or picture is produced 25 times per second).
   • Brightness variation is by changing number/intensity of electron beam.

4. (a) (i) to switch off all circuits
   (ii) the ring curcuit: B
         the lighting circuit: E
   (iii) thicker wire in ring circuit **or** two paths for current in ring circuit

   (b) (i) 2110 Ω
   (ii) 529 Ω

5. (a)

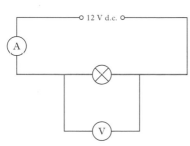

   (b) Resistance/R

   (c) (i) IV = 2 × 12 = 24
         $I^2R = 2^2 \times 6 = 24$
   (ii) Power
   (iii) Watt/W

6. (a) (i) half life = 13 hours
   (ii) because it is a Beta emitter and absorbed within the body **or** a gamma emitter is required to pass through body.
   (iii) larger dose required to kill the cancerous cells

   (b) Sievert (Sv)

7. (a) (i) The duration of the pulse, 10 microseconds, is very small **or** only prolonged exposure at this level will cause damage **or** 80 dB is threshold level for damage.
   (ii) 0.0225 m
   (iii) any stated value between 20 to 20 000 Hz

   (b) Ultrasound reflects off baby in womb and it takes different times to reflect from different depths of tissue. It is detected by receiver/computer.

8. (a) (i) light to electrical energy
   (ii) 1.2 V

   (b) (i) transistor (switch)
   (ii) 20 lux
   (iii) to protect the LED **or** to limit the current **or** to reduce the voltage across the LED

9. (a) $V_{in} = 0.06$ V

   (b) (i)

   (ii) 196 Hz

10. (a) No, as the average speed is **120 km/h** which is higher than speed limit.

   (b) Explanation must include the following:
   - car speedometer measures instantaneous speed
   - instantaneous speed will change during journey
   - average speed is measured over/greater time/whole journey.

11. (a) (i) 35 m/s²
   (ii) 980 000 N
   (iii) 710 000 N

   (b) (i) 59.2 MJ
   (ii) 128.75 m

12. (a) (i) shaking the torch makes the magnet move in and out of the coils **or** changing the magnetic field at coils by shaking the magnet
   (ii) The voltage will increase.
   (iii)

   (b) 14.4 C

   (c)

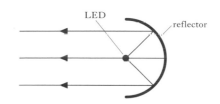

13. (a) 142 120 J

   (b) (i) 600 000 J
   (ii) 0.2 kg

14. (a) (i) P: X-rays
             Q: visible light
             R: microwaves
       (ii) gamma rays

    (b) infrared: thermometer **or** photodiode **or** phototransistor
        ultraviolet: fluorescent paint/material/UV film

15. (a) (i) 3.6 m/s^2 **or** 3.6 N/kg
       (ii) 2120 N

    (b) (i) 180 m
       (ii) 24 m/s

PHYSICS CREDIT 2008

1. (a) (i) 0.04 s

       (ii) new image is different from previous image
             the brain retains the image (while the new image is
             being displayed)

    (b) (i) red and blue
       (ii) red

2. (a) Period is 24 hours **or** always above the same point above
       the earth **or** period same as Earth

    (b)

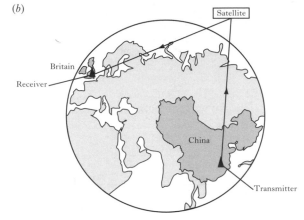

    (c) (i) 3×10^8 m/s
       (ii) 0.0375 m

3. (a) 0.02 s

    (b) The runner in lane 6 should have won because they took
        13.12 $(- 0.02 = 13.10)$ whilst the runner in lane 1 took 13.11
        seconds.

    (c) 2430 J

4. (a) (i) $I = \dfrac{V}{R}$ **or** $V = IR$ **or** $R = \dfrac{V}{I}$

            $= \dfrac{6}{120}$ $= 0.05 \times 120$ $= \dfrac{6}{0.05}$

            $= 0.05$ (A) $= 6$ (V) $= 120\ (\Omega)$

        ie it is resistor C

       (ii) direct reading **or** no need for calculation **or**
             easier (to obtain answer) or quicker

    (b) 880 Ω

5. (a) (i) cheaper / less current in each branch / thinner wire
       (ii) 230 V

    (b) (i) 0.435 A
       (ii) the current/power is too high so fuse could break if
             only one circuit **or**
             the fuse value is not enough for so many lamps

6. (a) (i) and (ii)

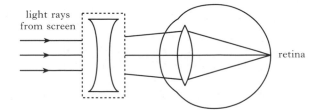

(b) (i)

    (ii) Fibre bundle X: transmits the light inside the patient
           Fibre bundle Y: transmits the reflected light/image
           back to the doctor's eye
    (iii) to allow the doctor to see/steer/manoeuvre to different
           parts of inside the body/the organ

7. (a) (i) time for the activity (or number of nuclei) (of a
           radioactive source) to reduce to half the original
           number/activity/its value
    (ii) 6 hours
    (iii) 10

  (b) windows allow different radiations to pass through
      film becomes fogged/blackened/darkened

8. (a) to limit current (flowing through LED) **or** prevent damage
     to LED

  (b) (i) 40 Ω
    (ii) 150 mA
    (iii) 0·45 W

  (c) *Any one from:*
    • uses less energy/power
    • more efficient
    • if one fails – others stay on

9. (a) (i) *Any one from:*
      • LDR
      • solar cell
      • photodiode

  (ii)

Music	Light level	X	Y	Z
off	dark	0	1	0
off	light	0	0	0
on	dark	1	1	1
on	light	1	0	0

  (b) (i) 9·8 W
    (ii) 2000
    (iii) 170 (Hz)

10. (a) $1·8 \times 10^7$ J

  (b) 90 m

  (c) energy is lost as heat energy **or** frictional heat losses **or**
     energy is lost because of friction

11. (a) (i) 1·25 m/s^2
    (ii) 112·5 N

  (b) 63·5 m

  (c) forces are balanced **or** 'forces are equal and opposite'

12. (a) (i) 1·1 MW

    (ii) (power) output not consistent **or** expensive **or**
          dangerous to build/maintain **or** few suitable locations

  (b) (i) 1 728 000 W

    (ii) heat losses in coils **or** magnetic losses in core **or** eddy
          currents in core

  (c) different water speeds **or** different sizes of rotor blades **or**
     different number of rotor blades

13. (a) in each reaction more neutrons are released and
      these cause further reactions

  (b) 150 000 (kg)

  (c) (i) (electromagnetic) coils produce moving/
          changing magnetic field voltage/
          current is induced in the (stator) coils
    (ii) Change 1: increase rate/speed of rotation
           Change 2: increase number of coils in (stator) **or**
                         (field) coils

14. (a) distance travelled by light in one year

  (b) (i) different detectors are required for different
          radiations/frequencies/ wavelengths
    (ii) C   A   B
    (iii) G-M tube **or** photographic film

  (c) (i) 2·5 D
    (ii) fainter objects can be observed **or** telescope gathers
          more light

15. (a) (i) friction (between craft and atmosphere causes heat
          production)
    (ii) 1300°C
    (iii) some heat (generated) is lost to surroundings **or** some
          heat energy reached the rest of the spacecraft

  (b) weighs less (in space)

PHYSICS CREDIT 2009

1. (a) (i) 3×10^8 m/s

(ii) $\lambda = \dfrac{v}{f}$

$= \dfrac{3 \times 10^8}{5 \times 10^9}$

$= 0.06$ m

(b) $v = 2 \times 10^8$ m/s

$t = \dfrac{d}{v}$

$= \dfrac{40000}{2 \times 10^8}$

$= 2 \times 10^{-4}$ s (0.0002 s)

(c) Carry more information
or less/no electrical interference
or cheaper
or larger bandwidth/capacity
or less amplifiers needed etc
or less repeaters required
or less signal loss
or lighter
or more secure (or similar)

2. (a) Sound waves with frequency above 20 000 Hz or 20 kHz **or** sound waves above/beyond the range of human hearing

(b) 1500 m/s

(c) $d = v \times t$
$= 1500 \times 0.36$
$= 540$ (m)

Must have unit if this is final answer

So depth $= \dfrac{540}{2}$
$= 270$ m

3. (a) Light (waves/signals) travels faster than sound (waves)
or sound waves travel slower than light waves

(b)

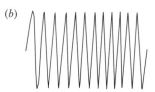

(c) $P_{out} = P_{gain} \times P_{in}$

$25000 \times 30 \times 10^{-3}$

$= 750$ W

4. (a) (i) Current increases
or gets bigger
or rises

(ii) A   position S
B   This position gives maximum <u>current</u>
or
this position gives least/minimum <u>resistance</u>
or
This position gives greatest/maximum <u>voltage</u>
<u>ACROSS</u> fan

(b) (i) The commutator ensures/keeps current (is) in the correct direction

or
Reverses/changes the direction of current every half turn
or
Keeps the coil rotating in the same direction

(ii) Carbon brushes do not wear (away) the commutator
or
Carbon brushes do not damage the commutator
or
withstand heat better
or
to allow low friction contact

(c) (i)

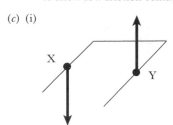

(ii) Reverse the magnetic field direction
or
Reverse current
or
Change the direction of the current

5. (a) Switch is connected to the neutral/blue wire
or
heating elements would always be live, even if switch is off
or
there is no fuse in the fire/the resistor should be a fuse
or
Blue (neutral) and brown (live) wires should be swapped
or
Blue (neutral) and brown (live) wires are wrong way round

(b) (i) Total power rating

$= 350 + 150 + 300$

$= 800$ (W)

Power$_{standby} =$
9% of 800 $= 800 \times \dfrac{9}{100}$

$= 72$ (W)

(ii) $E = P \times t$
$= 0.072 \times 14 \times 24$
$= 24$ (kWh)

6. (a) Hold lens between distant object and paper (or similar)
Use lens to focus/get sharp/clear image
Measure distance from lens to paper

(b) Refraction is when speed/wavelength changes
when the light travels into the material or lens/from one medium to another

(c) (i) and (ii)

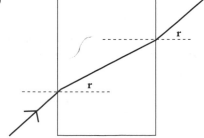

7. (a)

Type of radiation	Source
Beta only	C
Both alpha and gamma	B

(b) 4 half-lives
$18000 \rightarrow 9000 \rightarrow 4500 \rightarrow 2250 \rightarrow 1125$
Activity = 1125 Bq

8. (a) The voltage gradually rises
or increases
or reaches 6V

(b) Reduce value of resistor (R)/reduce resistance
Reduce value of the capacitor/reduce capacitance

(c) (i)
$$V_S = V_{LDR} + V_{53k\Omega}$$
$$6 \cdot 0 = 0 \cdot 7 + V_{53k\Omega}$$
$$V_{53k\Omega} = 5 \cdot 3 \text{ V}$$

(ii)
$$\frac{V_Q}{V_{53k\Omega}} = \frac{R_{LDR}}{R_{53k\Omega}}$$

$$\frac{0 \cdot 7}{5 \cdot 3} = \frac{R_{LDR}}{53000}$$

$$R_{LDR} = 7000\Omega$$

or

$$V_{LDR} = V_S \times \frac{R_{LDR}}{R_{LDR} + R_{53k\Omega}}$$

$$0 \cdot 7 = 6 \cdot 0 \times \frac{R_{LDR}}{R_{LDR} + 53000}$$

$$0 \cdot 7 \times (R_{LDR} + 53000) = 6 \times R_{LDR}$$
$$0 \cdot 7 \times 53000 = 5 \cdot 3 \times R_{LDR}$$
$$R_{LDR} = 7000\Omega$$

9. (a) LDR
or solar cell
or photodiode
or phototransistor

(b)

Gas	Sensor			
	A	B	C	D
Hydrogen	**0**	**1**	**0**	**1**
Helium	1	1	1	0
Oxygen	1	0	1	0

(c) (i) **or** gate

(ii) A $A = 0$
$B = 1$
$C = 0$
$D = 1$
B   hydrogen

10. (a) BC and DE

(b) (i)
$$W = m \times g$$
$$= 90 \cdot 0 \times 10$$
$$= 900 \text{ N}$$

(ii)
$$F_{res} = F_u - F_d$$
$$= 958 \cdot 5 - 900$$
$$= 58 \cdot 5 \text{ (N)}$$
$$a = \frac{F_{res}}{m}$$

$$a = \frac{58 \cdot 5}{90 \cdot 0}$$
$$= 0 \cdot 65 \text{ ms}^{-2}$$

11. (a)
$$a = \frac{v - u}{t}$$
$$a = \frac{0 \cdot 6 - 0}{1 \cdot 5}$$
$$= 0 \cdot 4 \text{ m/s}^2$$

(b) (i)
$$E_p = m g h$$
$$= 0 \cdot 02 \times 10 \times 0 \cdot 8$$
$$= 0 \cdot 16 \text{ J}$$

(ii)
$$E_p = E_k = 0 \cdot 16 \text{ J}$$
$$E = \frac{1}{2} mv^2$$
$$0 \cdot 16 = \frac{1}{2} \times 0 \cdot 02 \times v^2$$
$$v = 4 \text{ m/s}$$

12. (a) 220 000 N

(b) (i) distance = area under graph

$$= \left(\frac{1}{2} \times 240 \times 16\right) + (480 \times 16) + \left(\frac{1}{2} \times 480 \times 16\right)$$

$$= 1920 + 7680 + 3840$$
$$= 13440 \text{ m}$$

(ii)
$$v = \frac{d}{t}$$
$$= \frac{13440}{1200}$$
$$= 11 \cdot 2 \text{ m/s}$$

13. (a) To reduce power loss
or to reduce energy loss in the cables
or to reduce heat loss
or to reduce current

(b) (i)
$$\frac{N_S}{N_P} = \frac{V_S}{V_P}$$
$$\frac{N_S}{2000} = \frac{132000}{20000}$$
$$N_S = 13200 \text{ turns}$$

(ii)
$$\frac{I_S}{I_P} = \frac{N_P}{N_S}$$
$$\frac{I_S}{5000} = \frac{2000}{13200}$$
$$I_S = \frac{5000 \times 2000}{13200}$$
$$I_S = 758 \text{A}$$

or

$$V_P \times I_P = V_S \times I_S$$
$$20000 \times 5000 = 132000 \times I_S$$
$$I_S = 758 \text{A}$$

(c)
$$R = 220 \times 0 \cdot 31$$
$$(= 68 \cdot 2 \text{ } (\Omega))$$
$$P = I^2R$$
$$= 758^2 \times 68 \cdot 2$$
$$= 39 \cdot 2 \text{ MW}$$

14. (a)

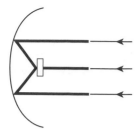

(b) E = c×m×ΔT

    = 902 × 8000 × (660 − 160)

    = 3 608 000 000 J

    (= 3·608 × 10⁹J (3·608 GJ))

(c) (i) l_f = 3·95 × 10⁵ (J/kg)

    E = ml

        = 8000 × 3·95 × 10⁵

        = 3·16 × 10⁹ J (3·16 GJ)

  (ii) P = $\frac{E}{t}$

    $800 \times 10^3 = \frac{3 \cdot 16 \times 10^9}{t}$

    t = 3·95 × 10³ s

  (iii) Heat is lost/radiated/escapes from the furnace
    or
    Heat is lost/radiated/escapes to the surroundings
    or
    Some of the heat energy is used to heat the container

15. (a) F = m × a

    $a = \dfrac{1400000}{(117000 + 8000)}$

    a = 11·2 m/s²

(b) Launch vehicle (uses fuel/jettisons stages so) loses <u>mass</u>
    or
    Less/no friction (from air)
    or
    Less/no air resistance
    or
    Weight is reducing due to fuel being used up/stages being jettisoned

(c) Answer should be based on the following two points:
    • statement relating to vertical motion, eg 'falling (towards the moon)', or force (of gravity)
    • statement relating to horizontal motion, eg 'probe moves forward', or curvature of Ganymede, eg 'surface curves away'

(d) Newton III:
    The thrusters force gas one way
    So the gas exerts an equal and opposite force on the probe.

16. (a) (i)

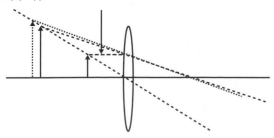

(ii) <u>Larger</u> diameter produces <u>brighter</u> image
    or converse

(b) (i) Radio waves are longer/greater/bigger/larger
    or light has a shorter wavelength

  (ii) Aerial
    or
    Radio telescope

  (iii) Different frequencies/wavelengths/signals require different detectors/telescopes
    or
    Certain detectors/telescopes can't pick up certain frequencies/wavelengths/signals

PHYSICS CREDIT 2010

1. (a) (i) 340 m/s

(ii) $\lambda = \dfrac{v}{f}$

$= \dfrac{340}{40000}$

$= 0\cdot0085$ m

(b) $t = \dfrac{d}{v}$

$= \dfrac{1\cdot7}{340}$

$= 0\cdot005$ s

time taken to return $=$ $2 \times 0\cdot005$
$=$ $0\cdot01$ s

(c) Decreases

2. (a) • Radio (signals/waves) have a longer wavelength than television (signals/waves)
• Longer wavelengths diffract more

(b) (i) 3×10^8 m/s
or
3 00 000 000 m/s

(ii) orbits the equator with a period of 24 hours
or
stays above the same point on the Earth's surface

3. (a) $I = \dfrac{1\cdot2}{2}$

$= 0\cdot6$ A

(b) $R = \dfrac{V}{I}$

$= \dfrac{3}{0\cdot6}$

$= 5\,0\ \Omega$

(c) $\dfrac{1}{R_T} = \dfrac{1}{R_1} + \dfrac{1}{R_2}$

$= \dfrac{1}{5} + \dfrac{1}{5}$

$R_T = 2\cdot5\ \Omega$

or

$R = \dfrac{V}{I}$

$= \dfrac{3}{1\cdot2}$

$R = 2\cdot5\ \Omega$

(d) $R_T = R_1 + R_2$

$= 2\cdot5 + 7\cdot5$

$= 10\ \Omega$

or

$R_T = \dfrac{V}{I}$

$= \dfrac{12}{1\cdot2}$

$= 10\ \Omega$

(e) (i) The ammeter reading will decrease
(ii) since the circuit resistance has now increased

4. (a) (i) To protect the flex

(ii) $I = \dfrac{P}{V}$

$= \dfrac{2530}{230}$

$= 11\cdot0$ A

(b) (i) Motor weighs less
or
field can be controlled
or
field is stronger

(ii) Motor turns more smoothly
or
is more powerful

(c) $E = P \times t$
$E = 1000 \times 60 \times 60$
$= 3\,600\,000$ J

5. (a) $P = \dfrac{1}{f}$

$= \dfrac{1}{0\cdot022}$

$= 45$ D

(b) (i) Short sight **or** myopia
(ii)

(iii) Rays are not focused on retina
or
rays are focussing in front of retina
or
rays do not meet/join at retina

(iv)

6. (a) (i) When an atom gains or loses negative charge
or
When an atom gains or loses electrons

(ii) Alpha
or
neutrons
or
x-rays
or
ultraviolet
or
cosmic rays

(b) $\dfrac{24}{8} = 3$ half lives

$6 \rightarrow 12 \rightarrow 24 \rightarrow \underline{48}$ MB$_q$

(c) (i) sieverts
or
Sv

(ii) Type of absorbing tissue
or
Absorbed dose
or
weighting factor
or
time

7. (*a*) Sensor resistance = 22 000 Ω

$$V_2 = \frac{R_2}{R_1 + R_2} V_s$$

$$= \frac{22000}{88000} \times 5$$

$$= 1\cdot25 \text{ V}$$

(*b*) (i) 9

(ii) $P = \dfrac{V^2}{R}$

$V^2 = 0\cdot147 \times 120$

$V = 4\cdot2 \text{ V}$

8. (*a*) (i) Lamp **or** LED

(ii)

Seat belt	Ignition	**P**	**Q**	**R**	**S**
unfastened	off	**0**	**1**	0	0
unfastened	on	**0**	**1**	1	1
fastened	off	**1**	**0**	0	0
fastened	on	**1**	**0**	1	0

(*b*) The driver will continue at constant speed until the seat belt applies an unbalanced force to stop the driver.

(*c*) (i) OR gate

(ii)

8. (*d*) thermistor or thermocouple

9. (*a*) $v = \dfrac{d}{t}$

$$= \frac{0\cdot06}{0\cdot075}$$

$$= 0\cdot8 \text{ m/s}$$

(*b*) $E_K = \dfrac{1}{2} mv^2$

$$= \frac{1}{2} \times 0\cdot55 \times 0\cdot8^2$$

$$= 0\cdot176 \text{ J}$$

(*c*) any *single* value greater than 0 m/s and **less than** answer given in part 9(*a*)

10. (*a*) (i) 0·6 s

(ii) distance = area under graph

$$= (8 \times 0\cdot6) + \left(\frac{1}{2} \times 8 \times 2\cdot2\right)$$

$$= 13.6 \text{ m}$$

(*b*) $a = \dfrac{F}{m}$

$$= \frac{150}{75}$$

$$= 2 \text{ m/s}^2$$

11. (*a*) I = 60 A

Q = It

$t = \dfrac{4500}{60}$

= 75 s

(*b*) percentage efficiency = $\dfrac{\text{useful Po}}{\text{Pi}} \times 100$

Input power = $120 \times \dfrac{100}{30}$

Input power = 400 W

(*c*) strength of magnet
or
number of turns in coil
or
speed of magnet

12. (*a*) (i) P = IV

= 12·5 × 230

= 2875(W)

$P = \dfrac{E}{t}$

E = 2875 × 180

E = 517500 (J)

or E = ItV

= 12·5 × 180 × 230

= 517500 (J)

(ii) c = 4180 (J/kg °C)

E = cm Δ T

m = 517500/(4180 × 72)

m = 1·72 kg

(iii) Some heat energy is transferred to the surrounding air
or
Some heat energy is transferred to the kettle parts

(*b*) (i) Temperature remains constant/same
or
temperature stays at 100°C

(ii) l = 22·6 × 10⁵ (J/Kg)

E = ml

$m = \dfrac{565000}{22\cdot6 \times 10^5}$

m = 0·25 kg

13. (*a*) Weight per unit mass
or
weight of/per 1 kg
or
Force per unit mass

(*b*) (i) $g = \dfrac{W}{m}$

$$g = \frac{630}{70}$$

g = 9 N/kg

(ii) Venus

(*c*) (i) $a = \dfrac{v - u}{t}$

$$1\cdot6 = \frac{(v - 0)}{1\cdot2}$$

v = 1·92 m/s

(ii) 1·2s

14. (a) (i) P Ultraviolet **or** uv

Q Infrared **or** IR **or**
thermal **or** heat rays

(ii) Gamma **or** γ

(iii) Aerial
or
radio telescope
or
satellite dish

(iv) Thermograms
or
electronic thermometer
or
treatment of muscle injury
or
sterilization (of equipment)
or
tracing
diagnosis of $\Big\}$ cancer
treatment of

(b)

Colour	Wavelength (m)
red	7×10^{-7}
yellow	$5 \cdot 9 \times 10^{-7}$
green	$5 \cdot 5 \times 10^{-7}$
blue	$4 \cdot 5 \times 10^{-7}$

(c) (i) $687 < \text{period} < 10\,760$ (days)

(ii) $v = 3 \times 10^8$ (m/s)

$t = \dfrac{d}{v}$

$= \dfrac{1430 \times 10^9}{3 \times 10^8}$

$= 4767$ s

1. (a) (i) 3×10^8 m/s
or 3 00 000 000 m/s

(ii) d = vt
$= 3 \cdot 0 \times 10^8 \times 0 \cdot 068$
$= 20400000$m

(b) $v = f\lambda$

$3 \cdot 0 \times 10^8 = 2100 \times 10^6 \times \lambda$

$\lambda = \dfrac{3 \cdot 0 \times 10^8}{2100 \times 10^6}$

$= 0 \cdot 14$ m

(c) A It gets louder/increases

Signal has a larger amplitude

B It/pitch gets higher/increases

$\begin{cases} \text{Waves are closer together} \\ \textbf{or} \\ \text{more waves are being produced in a certain time} \\ \textbf{or} \\ \text{Waves on graph are more frequent} \end{cases}$

2. (a) (i) White
(ii) Magenta

(b) (i) Rays of *light* are totally internally *reflected* inside the fibre

(ii) Carry more information
or
better signal quality

3. (a) $I = \dfrac{P}{V}$

$= \dfrac{60}{230}$

$= 0 \cdot 26$ A

(b) (i) $\dfrac{1}{R_T} = \dfrac{1}{R_1} + \dfrac{1}{R_2}$

$\dfrac{1}{R_T} = \dfrac{1}{46} + \dfrac{1}{92}$

$R_T = 30 \cdot 67 \ \Omega$

(ii) $P = \dfrac{V_2}{R}$

$= \dfrac{230^2}{30 \cdot 67}$

$= 1725$ W

Or calculate individual power of each heating element and
add together

(iii) S3

Greatest value of resis<u>tance</u>/lowest current/lowest power

4. (a) To switch off all circuits
or
To isolate the consumer unit fuses and domestic circuits from the mains supply

(b) (i)

Circuit	Value of fuse
Lighting Circuit	*5A*
Cooker	45A (given)
Ring Circuit	*30A*

(ii) The lighting circuit uses thinner cable

(c) Two routes for current to flow/less (half) current in each branch

or

Thinner cable/cheaper

(d) Reusable/faster response time/easily reset

5. (a) Convex

(b) (i) From graph,

$$t = \frac{1}{2} \times \begin{pmatrix} \text{back edge return} \\ \text{time} - \text{front edge} \\ \text{return time} \end{pmatrix}$$

$$t = \frac{1}{2} \times (13 \times 10^{-6} - 8 \times 10^{-6})$$
$$= 2\cdot5 \times 10^{-6} \text{ s}$$

(ii) $d = vt$
$$= 1500 \times 2\cdot5 \times 10^{-6}$$
$$= 0\cdot00375 \text{ m}$$

(c) (i)

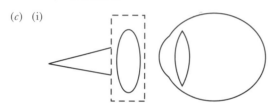

(ii)

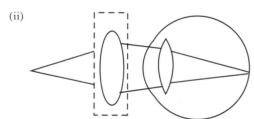

(iii) $P = \dfrac{1}{f}$

$$1\cdot4 = \frac{1}{f}$$

$$f = 0\cdot71 \text{ m}$$

6. (a) (i) Diagram 2 (represents ionised atom)
An electron has been removed (from the atom)

(ii) Alpha (α)

(b) Use tongs/don't point at eyes/wear gloves etc

(c) (i) Instrument sterilisation/treatment of cancer

(ii) Beta

(iii) A the same as
B Equivalent dose takes into account type of radiation

or

Both have equivalent dose
= 2mSv

7. (a) $V_1 = \dfrac{R_1}{R_1 + R_2} \times V_S$

$$= \frac{4000}{4000 + 60000} \times 12$$

$$= 0\cdot75 \text{ V}$$

(b) Transistor

(c) R of LDR increases
V across LDR increases (above 0.7V)
Transistor switches ON
Relay coil is energised (which closes the relay switch and activates the motor)

8. (a) (i)

P	Q	R	S
0	0	*1*	*1*
1	0	*0*	*0*
0	1	*1*	*1*
1	1	*0*	*1*

(b) (i) AND

(ii) When one of the inputs to gate X is logic 0
The output from gate X is logic 0

(iii) Loudspeaker

or

buzzer

or

Siren

or

bell

9. (a) (i) It is accelerating

or

Speeding up (NOT 'going down the flume')

(ii) distance = area under graph

$$= \frac{1}{2} \times 7\cdot5 \times 5 + 20 \times 5$$

$$= 18\cdot75 + 100$$

$$= 118\cdot75 \text{ m}$$

(iii) $a = \dfrac{v - u}{t}$

$$= \frac{15 - 5}{5}$$

$$= 2 \text{ m/s}^2$$

(b) measure time taken for log to pass a point.

measure the length of log.

use $v = \dfrac{d}{t}$ to calculate instantaneous speed

10. (a) (i) $W = mg$
$$= 35 \times 10^{-3} \times 10$$
$$= 0\cdot35 \text{ N}$$

(b) (i) 4·0 m/s

(ii) no unbalanced force so speed is unchanged

(c) (i) $E_K = \dfrac{1}{2} mv^2$

$$= 0\cdot5 \times 35 \times 10^{-3} \times 8\cdot0^2$$

$$= 1\cdot12 \text{J}$$

(ii) $Fd = \dfrac{1}{2} mv^2$

$$5\cdot0 \times d = 1\cdot12$$

$$d = \frac{1\cdot12}{5\cdot0}$$

$$= 0\cdot224 \text{ m}$$

11. (a) c = 4180 J/Kg°C from DATA SHEET

    E = $mc\Delta T$

       = $4180 \times 1 \cdot 6 \times 80$

       = 535040J

  (b) (i) l_v = $22 \cdot 6 \times 10^5$ (J\Kg)

      E = ml

       = $0 \cdot 9 \times 22 \cdot 6 \times 10^5$

       = 2034000J

    (ii) t = $\dfrac{E}{P}$

        = $\dfrac{2034000}{2000}$

        = 1017s

12. (a) E_P = mgh

      = $25 \times 10 \times 1 \cdot 2$

      = 300J

  (b) (i) P_{out} = $\dfrac{E}{t}$

         = $\dfrac{300}{60}$

         = 5 W

      Efficiency = $\dfrac{P_{out}}{P_{in}} \times 100$

          0·4 = $\dfrac{5}{P_{in}}$

          P_{in} = 12·5 W

    (ii) *Any two from:*

      Friction between the water and the inside wall of the plastic tube **or** heat energy is lost **or** sound energy is lost

13. (a) (i) package

    (ii) It moves with constant speed in the horizontal direction while accelerating due to the force of gravity in the vertical direction

  (b) g = 10 (m/s²)

    a = $\dfrac{v - u}{t}$

    10 = $\dfrac{v - 0}{0 \cdot 55}$

    v = 5·5 m/s

14. (a) (i) P ultraviolet

      Q infrared

      R microwaves

    (ii) TV and Radio

  (b) Cadmium and Mercury

15. (a) (i) If A exerts a force on B, B exerts an equal but opposite force on A.

      To every action (force) there is an equal and opposite

      or

      reaction (force)

    (ii) Engine/exhaust gases pushed down (A on B); gases push rocket up (B on A)

  (b) F_{UN} = ma

    8200 000 = $2 \cdot 05 \times 10^6 \times a$

    a = 4m/s²

Hey! I've done it

© 2011 SQA/Bright Red Publishing Ltd, All Rights Reserved
Published by Bright Red Publishing Ltd, 6 Stafford Street, Edinburgh, EH3 7AU
Tel: 0131 220 5804, Fax: 0131 220 6710, enquiries: sales@brightredpublishing.co.uk,
www.brightredpublishing.co.uk

Official SQA answers to 978-1-84948-189-0
2007-2011